THE STOOPING LADY

TO
H. B. H.
FROM WHOM IT CAME

CONTENTS

CONTENTS

THE STOOPING LADY

CHAPTER I

IN WHICH WE PLACE THE HEROINE

ON the 21st of January, 1809, Miss Hermia Mary
Chambre and her brother, Ensign Richard—as the
Countess of Morfa's chariot brought them for the first
time to Caryll House, St. James's, within those great
gates, into that gravelled court where the statue of a
late earl stood and admonished London*—on this day,
and on the very threshold of this Sanctuary of the Constitution, Miss Chambre, I say, and her brother, a beautiful and healthy girl of twenty and a fine young man
of rather less, were witnesses to a disagreeable incident,

---

* As this monument has now been removed, I feel bound to record
the inscription which it bore, long though it be.

ON
This Spot
where formerly stood
CARYLL HOUSE
and where
on the Fourteenth of October
1688
The Right Honourable
Rupert
Fourth Earl of Morfa Viscount Wrest
Baron Rhos and Ruegg K. G., Lord Lieutenant
and Custos Rotulorum of Flintshire etc. etc.
Returned Public Thanksgiving
to
Almighty God
For the Declaration of His Majesty

a vulgar brawl and scuffle, calling for the interference of the police.

Orphans, Irish by a deplorable father's side, and therefore in crying need of grace, this was the grace they got. Recalled within the pale of Family—that Family which their poor mother had forsworn—they were to see Family put to the blush. A rout of satyrs, a boors' comedy, in which an incensed young giant of the lower classes was hero and two tipsy gentlemen the sport of his heroics; in which Jacob Jacobs, elderly, gold-laced guardian of the gates, was choragus; in which footmen in canary yellow and powder, a groom of the chambers, a butler hovering for the carriage, took their cues from him, and wailed, lifted their eyes to Heaven, wagged their polls, called for constables, as he guided them with agitated hands—what a welcome to Britain! Beyond them and around them—with a ring scrupulously kept

---

King William III
That truly Constitutional Monarch
and
FATHER of his COUNTRY
This Statue
Has been erected by his admiring
Descendants to record for the
Elevation and Instruction
of
MANKIND
His Patriotism his Piety
and
His Prescience.

The lapidary has, in a pardonable enthusiasm, perhaps magnified his Lordship's act. What he is stated to have done upon the occasion recorded is to have slapped his thigh and said, "Thank God, we've dished the Tories!"

for the "turn-up"—surged and thundered the mob, intent only on the play, with raucous cries directed solely to that, with eyes afire for the rules of the great game. "Time! Time!" "Let my lord get his wind—Now they're at it—a mill, a mill!—ding-dong!" "What, you'll rush it, my lord? By God, that's stopped him!" "Six to one on the butcher—I lay." "Keep the ring, gentlemen, please—fobbed him fairly—gone to grass!" It was indeed at this crowning moment, when one gentleman lay bleeding on his back, and the other, slighter gentleman, "spitfiring like a tomcat," it was afterwards averred, struggled fruitlessly to escape the enemy's grasp of his coat-collar—that the family chariot of the Morfas loomed heavily at the far end of Cleveland Row and, advancing, displayed to the eyes of our young lady and her brother one of the sights of London—as they no doubt supposed it. Hardly seeing what, certainly, was not fit to be seen, no doubt for a second of time those startled eyes of hers gazed upon the havoc, and upon the flushed young Saxon, bareheaded and fair-headed, the hero of it—a noticeable young man performing noticeable feats with gentlemen. No doubt but that she too was by him gazed upon in her turn, and that that second of time seemed by seconds too long. These encounters of the eyes stay by one, though in this case there were sights to come. Within the gates lay another—a dead horse, weltering from the issue of a terrible wound; whereat indeed the bright-eyed Miss Chambre shrieked and clung to her brother, and he, after one sagacious look, said, "Staked, Hermy," and then, "Poor devil. So that was the meaning of it."

And thus 1809, thus London, thus England and Caryll House arrayed themselves to greet two young Carylls (by the mother's side) very newly from Ireland. A mob at the Gates! A dead and mangled horse within the Precincts! A tipsy gentleman scruffed by a butcher's man! The scene was significant. As the French would say— 1809!

The arrival of the carriage brought order back to some scattered wits. The canary-breeched footmen aligned in the vestibule, the groom of the chambers mounted the inner steps, the butler hovered for shawls. Servants of the Chambre pair—Gibson, a red-cheeked maid, and Simcox, a red-haired valet, descended from the rumble; Ensign Chambre, tall, slim, and lady-faced, got out and handed out his sister. "Here we are, my dear—Caryll House. What a shindy, eh? Let's get out of it all." But that was not possible to her.

"Oh, Dick, the poor horse—no, no! We must find out something. We can't possibly—" She turned to the butler, half in and half out of the carriage, collecting wraps. "What has happened? Who killed the horse? Who were those people? Please to let me know." The butler's head and shoulders came from the interior, deprecating inquiry; his hand humoured his chin. He really could not say; it was hardly for him to say. Per-

haps her ladyship—but he would inquire. Before he
could reach that last refuge of Secretaries of State and
butlers alike, Miss Chambre had turned to the powdered
array. Did any one see what it was? Was any one
present? Surely something was known? The giants
stiffened and stared; one was seen to blush, and another
betrayed, by a slight twitching of the fingers, that this
was the most awkward moment of his life. Miss Chambre's eyes, which were grey and very clear, insisted on
response; they had to be met. And so confused mutterings were heard, as one giant looked at the other, and deep
called unto deep. She caught the words—"His lordship"—"young Vernour"—"thirty-guinea 'oss"—"no
take-off for an 'oss," and "lashed 'isself into strips."
She was young, she was impatient, and used to obedience.
She stamped her foot.

"It's very extraordinary that nobody seems able to
speak here. I don't understand it at all." Then she
turned flashing upon the careworn butler. "Whose is
that horse?"

"I believe—they tell me, miss—it is young Vernour's
horse."

"Oh! And who is he?" The butler looked sideways.

"He's the butcher, miss."

"Oh, then that was he—that young man——"

"Yes, miss."

"And who were the other two, the two cowards attack-
ing him?"

But the butler's agony was now for all to see.

"I really—it's not for me, miss—but I'll inquire."

"Oh! Inquire!" She stamped again. Her brother was appealed to. Dick must go and find out; she insisted on knowing what was the matter; and while Dick stalked out to do her commands she chose to wait, tapping her foot in the vestibule, quite regardless of the canary-coloured giants about her, of hovering butler or groom of the chambers at his post. She had had no great experience of these gentry; she had lived in Ireland all her twenty years, and certainly her poor, pretty, helpless mother, Lady Hermione, whose runaway match with Colonel Chambre—Handsome Dick, Dick of the Gallop, and what-not—had been productive of little comfort besides these two children, certainly her mother had not been able to show her any such state. Why, except for McFinn—coachman in boots by day, footman in slippers by night—and the maids—three of them —there had been no indoor service at Chambre's Court. But there may have been traditions, and, of course, there was blood, to go upon. She had her Norman prerogative, *sa haulte franchise,* by the mother's side; and these stockinged emblems were so much furniture to her— now that she had found out that they could not pretend to be men. Not so to Gibson, her red-cheeked maid— but apparitors, wielders of the torture of silence and suspense. Gibson told her young mistress afterwards what she had endured in those awful moments of arrival. "If one of them yallows, Miss Hermy, had advanced a leg or put forth a finger, I should have died with the scream in my throat—so lifelike they was." One sees what she meant.

When Dick did return, he looked bothered.

"I can't make much of it out. They all talk at once. There was a row with a butcher about his horse—good horse, too—I could see that for myself. Somebody's been riding it, and staked it. Some gentleman, they say—or, at least, he thought so." Here he grew grave, reserved, made himself as old as he knew. "They do say —but I don't know anything about that. The horse is dead, the fellow's gone to gaol. The two gentlemen will prosecute. Their servants are with them, I believe. At any rate, they've been sent for. They weren't seriously hurt, either of them. I say, Hermy, I do think we might go in—now, you know."

But Miss Hermia had opened her eyes, and wouldn't budge.

"To prosecute, my dear! To prosecute the butcher! How can they prosecute him for staking his own horse?"

"You don't understand me. He didn't stake the horse. I thought I had made that clear."

She did not choose to see. "Very well, then, I suppose they will prosecute him for owning a horse at all. Is that what you mean?"

Dick put on his Ensign's manner—his last refuge against this sort of attack. "Why, you see, my love, it is rather an awkward business. The fellow began it. Of course, the whole affair might have been settled if he had taken it reasonably."

"Reasonably!" Really, for a girl only two years his senior, she caught him up. "How do you take a s⸀ ̇ked horse reasonably?"

"My dear child, this fellow had hold of a gentleman— of a peer, they say—by the collar, and gave the other no end of a smack on the nose. Well, you know, you can't have that, can you?"

Miss Chambre, after staring at her brother for a trying moment, turned her back upon him, and walked up the array to the house. She threw him a Parthian shot. "You can have what you deserve—and be called a gentleman—and not take it like a gentleman—or so it seems."

Dick followed her nervously. He knew his sister, but he knew more. He knew the names of the two gentlemen; she must never get at them, whatever happened. But he had his birthright in him, too. "One was a peer, remember—and the other a peer's eldest son. I can't say any more. And they were both drunk—you ought to remember that." She marched on.

"Pooh!" she threw at him, "I don't believe you. And if it's true, it makes it all horrible."

"They were drunk as owls," says Ensign Dick.

"As pigs, you mean," flung back the lady.

The groom of the chambers mutely implored—his long white face was a study in the tragic: that of a just man

and-water; she got some bread and milk. Simcox and poor, dear Gibson had been dreadfully ill—prostrate! Simcox said that never, in his born days—but she here perceived that Lady Morfa took no interest in Simcox or his days, and pursued her own adventures. What did grandmamma think? It was rather a wet morning, but not very; so she and Dick rode *outside* the coach, and put the servants inside. It had been the greatest fun—they saw the dawn, but not in England as they had hoped, for they were still in Wales. The coachman was very kind. He told the guard that Dick was "a bit o' blood," and the guard had said, "Bless your life, that liquor's bound to show"—wasn't that fun? It was three in the morning when they were off, and not a soul out of bed, once past the inn-yard.

She touched but lightly on the landscape, flashed upon by the coach-lamps and swiftly blotted out; slumbrous villages, shaly banks, lanes endless and tortuous, long ascents and breakneck gallops down into blackness, gaunt finger-posts to hidden ways—a chance-caught "To Chester," another "To Carnarvon," and then "To Ruthin," where lay, she knew, Morfa Mawr, the cradle and chief seat of all the Carylls—dripping trees, rivers, narrow bridges. She had lived through the dark upon these, but they were not for her tongue to tell of. Nor how, when the five dark hours had been past, and with the pale winter sun striving with the rain, they had looked out upon the heart of Wales—and there was Ogwen Lake,

all black under the storm-cloud, and all that litter and
slide so shining wet under the splintered mountain: a
quarry of slate! Not for her untried speech all this.
She spoke rather of their fellow passengers, and as one
who knew them well; the young usher for Rugby, with
a painful catch in his breath, who had shown her the portrait of his mother; the sea-captain homing to wife and
child at Wem; the wine-merchant whose head had nodded
on to her shoulder, and whose apologies had been so
frequent and profound; and, lastly, and with fervour,
she told of Mr. Aloysius Banks. Kind! He had been
more than kind—he had gone out of his way to be kind
—and had accompanied them to London.

"Do you mean," asked Lady Morfa here, "that this—
ah, person—was going out of his way when he came on
to London?"

Miss Hermia was not so innocent as to fail to understand what Lady Morfa meant by a "person."

"He's not a person—what you would call a person—
grandmamma, at all. And, of course, he lives in London. I am surprised that you don't know him—indeed,
he told me that you did. He had met you at Lady
Crowland's, he said. He was able to do you some tri-
fling service. You bowed. There can be no mistake.
Mr. Aloysius Banks, an Edinburgh Reviewer."

Grandmamma may have meant to name Mr. Banks a
personage, but did not look as if she had. She denied
his acquaintance. Miss Chambre sketched him freehand.

He was extraordinarily ugly, and seemed to feel the cold. His eyebrows looked very odd when the rime was thick upon them. He wore a plaid scarf so tightly round his neck that Dick had said, and she could not but agree, that he looked like a skull tied up in crossbones. He had been snappish at first, but they had done their best to make him happier, and she believed they had succeeded. Nobody could have been kinder than he. He was a poet and critic—most severe—but that was forced upon him. He was a Whig, of course; and he said that all the Ministerial poets, and, above all, the Jacobin poets, were so deplorably bad that he felt it his duty to be stringent. When, said he, you find principle as lax as numbers, morals and sense alike subverted; when your rhymester is as trite as he is obscure, adds factiousness to dulness, and turns all to blasphemous uses—it is no time for lovers of order to be silent. He had been charged, he said, but unjustly charged, with having caused one young man to die of mortification, or (as he hoped it might be said) of remorse. Mr. Banks added that he hoped that he should never shrink from his duty to the Constitution, however painful that duty might be. He had the profoundest respect for the Constitution and for great families. Anecdotes! He had one for every fine house he passed. There was Sir Tancarville Tancarville's: he had married his cook. Stokeheaton's mansion reminded him of a very sad affair—how young Lord Wilmer had called out Colonel Despard, and how the Colonel had shot him; Mr. Banks had to be excused the reason. Then there had been Lady Diana Meon, who ran away with——

"And we saw Wolseley Hall, grandmamma, where papa had often stayed, with Sir Charles. They saw the fall of the Bastille together, you know—but I forgot! You didn't agree with papa about that. Nor did Mr. Banks, by any means." Lady Morfa considered that that was the best thing she had heard of Mr. Banks so far; but she did not say so. She was learning this free-spoken granddaughter of hers.

On the whole, it seemed that Mr. Banks was at his best upon the subject of noble birth and what he called "Franchise." What had he meant by that, precisely? Miss Chambre had asked him. He had explained. Franchise was the liberty which blood conferred, and, in these days, place, since the King, we must not forget, was the Fountain of Honour, and could ennoble by a look. So franchise was liberty—the liberty to be free, and the liberty to rule a free people—a harmony, not a discord of ideas. "I found that difficult," said Miss Hermia. "I asked him what gave the liberty to rule, and he said Place; what gave Place, and he said Blood." It was puzzling, because there was another kind of Franchise—a parliamentary kind, which Mr. Banks refused to discuss, which seemed to make him angry, which, he said, had nothing to do with true Franchise. But let grandmamma consider. A free people had the freedom

to be ruled; Blood and Place had the freedom to rule."
She frowned now as she thought of it, but grandmamma
refused to help. "Bits of blood," were they, had said the
coachman to the guard. And then she remembered the
butcher's horse. There had been blood there, too.

All that apart, she owned that she had found Mr.
Banks's eulogy of the Carylls rather fulsome. "He knew
who we were without our having to tell him. He said
that the country still mourned grandpapa, and that
Uncle Roddy was very high in the confidence of the
Prince of Wales. And then he spoke of you, grandmamma, and of Uncle Badlesmere, and of all your
family. He said that the Botetorts and the Carylls bore
the only shields that remained unsullied in England. I
told him that I thought that impossible, and that if it
were true he ought not to say it to us. Perhaps I ought
not to have gone so far—Dick thought not. But he was
very charming in what he said about you."

Lady Morfa took Mr. Banks's charms as best she might.
She went so far as to ask what the gentleman had been
pleased to say of herself, and accepted with grim
acquiescence a tribute to "that combination in her ladyship's person of exalted birth and enlightened principles
which set England, our happy country, apart from all
European nations." If her granddaughter did not
report him exactly, that is what he had said. Miss
Chambre remembered also how he had praised Mr. Fox,
the Dukes of Bedford and Devonshire, Lord Lansdowne,

Lords Grey and Grenville. Lord Crowland he was proud
to call his Mæcenas. All this should have endeared him
to Lady Morfa, for all these were her allies; but she was
staggered with what followed. Miss Hermia, owning
that she knew nothing of these gentlemen, had asked him
concerning others—"friends of papa's"—with less happy
results. "When I asked him," she said, "if he had
known Lord Edward, he said 'Good God!' and had no
more to say."

"I don't wonder," said Lady Morfa, and, like Mr.
Banks, said no more; for Lord Edward could only be
Lord Edward Fitzgerald, whom she was accustomed to
describe as "that little renegade who married the
Frenchwoman," and who signified for her the three
things in this world most detestable—enthusiasm, slackness of fibre, and treachery. She kept a keen ear for
Miss Hermia's chatter after that; but all went passably
well until the end.

"And so, grandmamma, we got to London at last, and
met the carriage, and oh! I must tell you of a most disagreeable thing—which I think you ought to know
about."

Out it came, the whole of it, and Lady Morfa bristled
and stiffened as she heard. A staked horse! The battle
at the gates! The ring, the prostrate gentleman.
"Dick tells me he was a gentleman, but I can't believe
that. He was tipsy, and one of two. The other I
couldn't see, because the butcher had him by the coat-

collar; he was tipsy, too, and, Dick says, a peer. He was using very bad language, but couldn't possibly get away. The butcher was a splendid young man." And then she added, "His eyes give him that proud look. I mean that they see you, and see that you are nothing."

"You are talking sad rubbish, my dear," said Lady Morfa with decision. "What's all this? I've heard nothing of it."

Dick Chambre, very red and uncomfortable, put in his word. "I don't think it need disturb you, ma'am. It was some vulgar attack. They sent for the constables, and, no doubt, it's all over. I think Hermy was upset."

If she was, it became her. It gave her starry eyes and a colour of flame; it lifted her head and gave a thrill to her voice. "No one can bear injustice," she said. "It's horrible. Oh, grandmamma, what do you think? They've taken the man to prison because they staked his horse. Why, papa would have— Oh, grandmamma, what can we do?"

Lady Morfa, after blinking and working her tightened lips, put an end to the conversation. "We can do a number of things, my dear, and one of them is to refrain from discussing subjects of which we know little or nothing. If you will kindly ring the bell, I'll have you shown your rooms. I'm an old woman, as you see, and not above owning when I'm tired. Ring the bell, my child."

Miss Hermia was taken in convoy by the housekeeper; but Ensign Dick remained to show his commission, for which he had to thank his grandmother, to talk of the Army of Portugal, which he was soon to join, of the levee, of uniforms, of his horses, and other glories of youth. He was a simple, well-spoken lad, much to her ladyship's taste. She liked young men to be good-looking, to call her "ma'am," and to agree with her. These were Caryll qualities; and she could manage the Carylls, or, at least, had never met with one whom she could not. Dick Chambre proved no exception, and with his help she flattered herself that she could deal with the girl. The girl was Chambre—that was evident; but Lady Morfa meant to do her duty by her. What was this wild story of the butcher's horse? What had Dick to say about that? The unhappy Dick had much to say which nothing would have induced him to reveal. That she guessed; therefore, after letting him flounder and blush into coherence, she gave him his orders. "My dear boy, it's clear that you have great good sense. These vulgar things are not to be wondered at in the time we live in; insubordination, however, must be checked. I remember that I speak to a soldier. Your sister is excited because she is tired. To-morrow she will have forgotten all about it. Give her my love, and say that I shall excuse her at dinner to-night. Let her have her sleep out—she shan't be called in the morning. And let us have no more talk of fighting butchers and their horses. Truly, a 'splendid' young man! Remember, Richard, we must have no more wild speeches. And the less of your Mr.

Aloysius Banks the better. Progers will show you your quarters if you ring. You will find your man, no doubt." So away with Ensign Richard and his commission.

But her ladyship had more to do. After a time of bleak survey of the fire, she rang her handbell. Progers, the careworn butler, the velvet-footed, came in.

"Ah, Progers," said the lady, "has his lordship returned?"

"Yes, my lady. His lordship have returned. His lordship have asked me to say that he is feeling himself indisposed, and will not dine."

"No, no. I will see his lordship presently. Has Dr. Noring been sent for?"

"Dr. Noring is here, my lady. He is with his lordship."

"Very well. That will do, I think. And—ah, Progers——"

"My lady?"

"There was, I understand, a disagreeable scene this afternoon. Vernour, the butcher, was concerned in it."

"Yes, my lady." Progers of the furrowed brow!

"Let orders be given that Vernour is not to call again for custom. Let that be done at once. And let there be no talking about this, if you please. Miss Chambre was greatly upset by the affair. I don't wish anything said to Miss Chambre—or to anybody in the house. Understand that, Progers."

"Very good, my lady."

Dr. Noring reported that the young Earl of Morfa
was suffering from a severe shock to the nervous system,
and must have rest. A low diet could do no harm; but
rest was imperative.

CHAPTER III

IT is possible that the annals of the politicians may en-
shrine the person of a stauncher Whig than that of
Jane (born Botetort) Countess of Morfa, but if they
do I have never heard of it. It is highly improbable; she
was not only all that a Whig should be, she was all that
he could ever be and remain a man. She was a Whig of
the Whigs, dotting all the *i's* in the sacred words *British
Constitution;* she was Whiggism incarnate, for she added
character to principle, and what she professed, that she
was. Where Mr. Fox had doubted, she had affirmed;
where Lord Crowland shook his head, she shook her fist;
where my Lord Grey was tempted to enquire, she held her
nose. Thus she was the sublimity of the Whig position,
which was not one of compromise, but of despair. For
the Whigs took kings into favour, not because they were
estimable, but because without them the families could
not govern; and though many of them may have believed it, and some may have said it, I know of none to
whom it was so much bone of the bone as to Lady Morfa,
of none who said it so stoutly and lived it so hard as she
did.

She divided mankind, for all purposes, into two classes.

Either you were Family, or you were a person. Collectively, you were still Family, unless you were the Mob. It's true she allowed, for convenience, of a third possible class in which either of the categories might be temporarily embraced. If, being Family, you happened to earn your living by sword or pen, she might, in her gentler moments, refer to you as of the Executive; if, being of the Mob, you should raise your head by such means into her notice, she would undoubtedly—for she was as incisive as she was frank—call you a Hireling. Here, then, was a sort of limbo for Society, into which fell, naturally, Kings, Archbishops, Secretaries of State, and others—admittedly a makeshift, and due to the complexity which the French Revolution had introduced, whereby a Mr. Canning and a Lord Castlereagh might labour side by side.

In 1809, when we first make her acquaintance, she was in her seventy-second year, and the twentieth of her widowhood; she had married all her daughters—one of them, Miss Chambre's mother, had, to be sure, done that for herself—and was still queen of Caryll House, St. James's, and of all the Caryll Castles and demesnes, until such time as Earl Roderick, her only son and her last-born, should marry into Family and reign alone. In person she was thin, not tall, and very much like an eagle, with a nose sharp, bony, and prominent, with eyes black, hard, and deeply set, which were capable of unswerving, unblinking, and rather terrible scrutiny of persons and things. She could blink them too, bitterly, when she chose; and her lips, which were thin, had a way of twitching very elfin to behold. Lastly, she stooped to a crutch, called you "My dear," said exactly what she pleased, never concealed her opinions, and was absolutely candid as to her tastes, which were coarse, and her abhorrences, which were three. I have mentioned them before: enthusiasm, slackness of fibre, and treachery to Family. These things really disgusted, and one of them really shocked her. Have I spoken of her religion? She was punctilious in that matter, for she was, of course, an Erastian. It was a question of drill.

Her parties were renowned, not for their brilliancy of talk—she smelt enthusiasm in good talkers—but for their severe exclusion of all but the purest of the pure. The Executive were on their best behaviour there, you may well believe. It was said that in certain lights a faint but exquisite tinge of azure was to be seen floating over her thronged assemblies, like a bloom upon a budding coppice; a shot effect, an irradiance, an aural shimmer of blue. I can easily believe it, but (since even Lady Morfa was human and her parties must be slightly tainted with that failing), I prefer another similitude, which has been happily used of them. Imagine a fish-pond, one of those ovals of dark, still, and lilied water, marble-rimmed, which you find in old gardens of statues, cypress walks, and deep turf. Just as in that the carp vary in perfection; while some are of the ruddiest gold, some unfortunately have silver splashes, and some again are so scored with the paler metal that the gold and silver seem to have changed places, and some even have no gold visible, but show all of silver—yet all are undoubted gold-fish, by an ancestry which cannot be denied: so it was in Lady Morfa's drawing-rooms, that though all her guests were Whigs by origin and men of Family by grace, some were speckled with radicalism, and some desperate players speckled only now with the remnants of Whiggery, and some had so basely handled themselves that, but for species, no sign remained. Among these variegated ones are some whom we must reckon with. We may pass Lord Henry Petty by, although he must be a Marquis before our tale is done. But there swam my Lord Sandgate, all gleaming silver, there another white renegade, Captain the Honourable Robert Ranald of the Navy—Member for Westminster, but so finely descended and so much a man that his pedigree and (what was odd) his virtues tinged his coat in her Ladyship's eyes. There, too, much at his ease, came and went Lord Rodono, parcee gilt, but saved by a fine gift of raillery. At all of these, and at others like them, whom to name would be tedious—Mervyn Touchett, Pink Mordaunt, Gell-Gell, Lord Drillstone, and their friends—the Lady of Caryll House looked through rose-coloured glasses, which lent them charitable pretence. But those pale fish beyond them—your baronets Wolseley and Burdett, your Squires Whitbread and Colonels

Wardle—"my dear, those are impossible persons. I will
not know them, and there's an end. As well ask me to
have in Cobbett—that man—or your Major Cartwright
or precious Parson Tooke." Them you never, never
saw in the unruffled pool, where great Cavendish, great
Russell, great Crowland, and great Vane oared the deep
on golden fins. To be sure, she made an exception—
pour rire—in favour of Lord Stanhope, the big-nosed,
brawny, long-armed peer—Citizen Stanhope of his own
dubbing. Him she let in, as Samson of old was led, to
make sport. "Citizen?" she had said, "yes, indeed, that
is what the poor man has made of himself. Have him,
by all means." She called him Citizen before he could
call her one, and never called him anything else until
he sickened, and loathed the term. What is more, she
treated him as she would have treated an alderman or a
royal duke—as he knew very well.

I find that I have very little to say of the young Earl
Roderick, her son. Born late, he had grown up sickly
and passably vicious. He was twenty-five years old,
Equerry to the Prince of Wales, a Knight of the Garter,
and unpopular. Up to the time when this tale begins
he had done nothing commendable, and a good deal of
which I shall be charitably silent. He had the reputa-
tion of being niggardly, and Mr. Sheridan is said to
have hated him. The two things are by no means in-
compatible, and are very likely connected.

But I want to direct your attention to the Chambre

connection, which is of serious moment to you who read, and was the heaviest blow ever dealt at the doughty Countess of Morfa. Miss Chambre was in this position: Lady Morfa was her grandmother and practically her owner for a term of years yet to come. Colonel Chambre, her father, had never had a shilling, not even on the day when he ran off with Lady Hermione Caryll, her mother, made a Scots marriage of it, and prepared to be happy; but that Lady Hermione had had some thousand pounds a year in her own right. When Colonel Chambre died, in 1807, his widow was not long in following him—and yet she was not soon enough for his children's liberties. For between his death and her own, my Lady Morfa interposed a dictatorship, spending a year in Ireland for the purpose, with the result that Lady Hermione disposed of her thousand as follows. Dick, her son, was to have half when he came of age. If he died unmarried, his portion was to be added to the other. But Hermia's share and contingency were not to be hers until she was five-and-twenty, or married with the consent of her grandmother. If she died under that age, or married after the fashion of her mother, her five hundred, or whatever more she might have, was to return into the coffers of the Carylls, whence it came. The money was paltry enough, but the tutorship was not— and that was what Lady Morfa was after. She did not intend, if she could help it, that Hermione's girl should grow up either a pure fool like her mother, or a fool

adulterated with knave, as she was convinced Colonel
Chambre, her father, must have been. He was a man
whom she as heartily despised as she heartily hated;
and certainly, from her point of view, the Colonel's
record was not comfortable. He was both enthusiastic
and a traitor to Family. He could only have had one
other vice—and Lady Hermione had that, poor soul!

Colonel Richard Chambre—Dick, Handsome Dick,
Firebrand Dick, Dick of the Gallop, all these things
they called, who loved, him—was a cadet of a good English house settled in Ireland in the planting times. As a
boy he had read as he rode, as a young man in the —th
Foot, if he had a sword in his right hand he had a book
in his left. Yet he served with distinction in the American War, got his steps rapidly and with dash, and might
have risen high but for two things. At Charleston he
came to love Lord Edward Fitzgerald, and it was a fault
(I suppose) of his nature to desire to be that which he
loved. Hence he found himself sympathising with the
rebels, and as good as a rebel himself. Tom Paine did
the rest for him. There was no half-way house for the
likes of Handsome Dick; he broke his sword, he threw up
his commission; they say that it was Lord Edward—with
a bright eye on France—who persuaded him not to bear
arms against his own blood in a quarrel whose issue was
certain, but to keep them unrusted, rather, against the
time coming. But for that he would either have settled
in America or died for the Americans. As things were,

he returned to Europe with his beloved friend, with him in due course went into France, improved acquaintance with Tom, and shared in the great design of re-making Britain as the Rights of Man demanded. His English adventures were not happy, as revolutionaries conceive of happiness. The last king was not hanged in the entrails of the last priest; no blood was shed, but quantities of ink; even the honours of an indictment for sedition were denied him. He consorted with Godwin, and found him squalid, with Mr. Tooke, and thought him unpardonably dry. However, from that gentleman's house at Wimbledon he did concoct a private adventure, with danger in it, excitement, and, as it turned out, with fruit. From Wimbledon it was that he rode into London on a still summer's night in 1788, tethered his horse, scaled the wall of Caryll House garden, and affixed to it a rope-ladder. At the stroke of midnight pretty Lady Hermione, all blushes, terrors, and fluttered heart, fell panting into his arms. He had met her, it seems, but three times in his life, had loved her at sight, and found means to make her love him. He helped her over the wall, put her up behind him, and galloped away to Finchley and an awaiting carriage. Dick of the Gallop—this feat was the occasion of the nickname. At Carstairs, in Scotland, he proclaimed her his before God and the innkeeper's family; he took her to Roscommon and his house of Chambre's Court; and next year Hermia Mary was born into the world—a daughter of debate—one hun-

dred and one years to a day since Rupert Earl of Morfa
had thanked God publicly for the British Constitution.

The subsequent feats of Galloping Dick did nothing to
reconcile him to his mother-in-law. He went back to
France, and (Lady Morfa believed) procured the fall of
the Bastille; he showed himself in England in 1794, and
was only saved from the High Treason trials of that year
by the fact that he was full of schemes for a rebellion in
Ireland. The failure of that, its tragic absurdity, its
treacheries, hidings, women's clothes, and bedside arrests,
above all, the death in delirium of the adored and ador-
able little incendiary at the heart of it, went near to
breaking Chambre's own heart, and quite broke his spirit.
He galloped no more, but cultivated his few acres, bred
foxhounds, and gave his children of his best. Hermia
Mary (as he always called her) was his favourite; I
believe he told her everything he had ever done—and he
might well do that, for he had no reason to blush for his
misdeeds. He had ever been too ardent to have time for
rakehelling; he ate vegetables, and drank water with
his wine. Towards the end of his life he took to
prophecy, stroking his girl's hair or playing gently with
her hand. He had hopes that she would in her person
justify all that he had loved and served in the world.
Should she, the child of Privilege, show Privilege powerless, before the Rights of Man! That was his prophecy.
"I see you a woman grown, my child; I see you a lover.
Manhood—womanhood—and the call of the heart be-

tween; you will never be false to that. Love worthily, love well, love the best. Love truth, love justice, my Hermia Mary; hate like the devil those three children of his—Cant, False Privilege, and Treachery to the Truth that is in you." Pretty sentiments these for a man to die in, connected by marriage with the House of Caryll! Pretty for Jane Countess of Morfa to see the fire of them still smouldering in his girl's grey eyes. But there it was, though guarded, when that beaked great lady came to Roscommon in 1807.

She came in her chariot and four, like an eagle that had scented carrion from afar and had swooped directly the watchers had departed. Pretty, tearful Lady Hermione —if she were a watcher—had resigned without a struggle to the rape of her nestlings; young Dick, a more delicate image of his father, fair-haired, slim, and falcon-like as he had been, swallowed his ensigncy and became a noble Whig; but Hermia Mary kept an open mind. She, too, had something of her father— his hot colouring and his dark grey eyes—but in all else resembled the Carylls. She had their dark tresses, their easy carriage, bold voice, and imperious judgments; she was afraid of nobody, and always spoke the truth. All these things commended her to her grandmother, who loved her order, loved beauty, and loved courage, even when displayed at her own expense. This girl fulfilled all her loves; she had remarkable beauty of face and person, she showed Family

to the finger-tips; and she had wit. Lady Morfa left
Ireland full of promises; Dick was to have his ensigncy
—that would get rid of Dick; but Hermia Mary was to
be brought out in London, a Caryll beauty and a Caryll
heiress—she would see to that. The times were hopeful.
The old king was known to be incurable, the Prince
would be Regent. His friends were her friends. There
would be a Whig administration, and—here we see the
finger of Providence—a child of the House of Caryll
would again be Maid of Honour, as she had not been
since 1689. Thus Lady Morfa conceived that the Gods
of England would dispose and govern the hearts of
princes whom the Whigs had set up. One might credit
them with more grandiose designs; but there is a story
of an Eastern mystic which is to the point.

This enthusiast, they say, chose out for himself a place
in the desert under a palm-tree; and lying there supine
and entirely naked, concentrated his sight upon his own
navel, and at last, after some thirty years' toil, had the
reward of seeing the whole wheeling order of the Cosmos
—all Time and all Existence—centred and revolving
about that fixed point. And whether your Whig states-
man hide himself behind the ramparts of the British
Constitution and its spiky frieze of privilege, or within
the walls and double gates of Caryll House, St. James's,
he is apt to mistake Providence for the gardener, and to
see in the soft-footed messengers of his chambers Angels
and Ministers of Destiny.

When Hermia Mary left Ireland it was said that she had emptied the county of its most beautiful woman. It may well be so. I have seen her portrait by Lawrence, which gives a face of high seriousness and rich hues of carmine, ivory, and dark brown. Her figure is certainly exquisite, her hair like a sable cloud. Her rivals in Dublin, and afterwards in London, used to say that she had too much composure for a *débutante*. They all implied by that that she had her own ideas.

CHAPTER IV

CARYLL HOUSE, a great pile of building in the Augustan style, stood in its own garden, surrounded by its own spiked wall, and abutted on the Green Park, as nearly as I can judge, somewhere south of the Bridgwater House of our day. You drove in from Cleveland Row between a fine pair of wrought-iron gates, which dragon-crested pillars upheld, which a porter in a lodge jealously guarded, and which no commoner might pass unquestioned and alive. It was said of this porter that he had never, in a service of thirty years, been mistaken in a peer or a peer's son, though he admitted in moments of confidence that he was not so sure as he had been of third generations. Jacob Jacobs was the name of this valuable Argus, and he had been given to understand his value. Once a year, on Saint George's Day, he was bidden to the house by the steward, received into the housekeeper's room, where wine and cake stood upon the table; and after an interval of not more than half an hour, heralded by two footmen and the butler, Lady Morfa herself appeared, leaning on the arm of her appointed companion for the time. All rose to their feet. The butler advanced to the table, poured out a glass of brown sherry, and handed it to her ladyship. She took it, and herself handed it to Jacob Jacobs, who received it with a profound salutation and a careful bow. Meantime, the housekeeper had cut up the cake. "Jacobs," said her ladyship, "I desire that you will drink this to the health of the House. It is Saint George's Day."

"I thank your ladyship kindly," was the time-honoured reply. "Here's Fame to the House and stability to the British Constitution." Those are difficult words—we know they were made a test case for topers—but Jacob Jacobs had never failed in them yet. He drained his glass, and handed it back to his lady, who retired. The cake and wine might then be consumed by the assistants at the ceremony, no one of whom had ever been graced so highly as this. Once, many years ago, the house-steward (father of the man of 1809) had led her lady-ship out in Sir Roger de Coverley. But that had been after the christening of his present lordship—and that had been in the country, where manners are more relaxed.

These particulars will serve to show what kind of state was maintained within that massy approach guarded by the privileged Jacobs, and perhaps to explain the fact that it was found to be excessively irksome by Miss Hermia Mary, after the slippered ease, the hunt-break-fasts, the barehead-scampers, and firelight readings of Chambre's Court, after the domestic calm—chicken-rearing, egg-marking, gardening, and what-not of her more recent experience, in the home of Cousin Mary Fox, at sweet Kilbride. In an early letter to this lady—always her dearest friend— we catch some hint of it. "A giant to each door, and a row of white-headed, flaming-breeched giants in the gallery; a groom of the chambers to herald any silly errand to grandmamma—vexatious, Mary! I feel like a parcel from the country—fresh butter, perhaps—handed about from man to man, from coach to coach, and delivered at last, greasy and thumbed, to my purchaser. She, of course, gives me over to a secretary or a maid to be opened and put away.

"Oh, Mary, Mary," she wails in her comical way, "we have six men to feed us, and each man has his office. One hands clean plates, one must touch dirty plates only; if the butler has toothache, nobody can have any wine. At least, I suppose not, but as yet he has escaped it. We have a clergyman to say our prayers for us—who says twice a day, 'Thou Who didst bring order out of chaos, and say unto Thine Elect, *Come, ye blessed*, and unto others, *Depart ye*, bless this noble family, which Thou hast set up, prosper it exceedingly,' &c., &c. Upon my honour, Mary! And instead of my dear old Gibby to sit on my bed and scold me while I get ready for it, I am now undressed and put there by a Mrs. Moth, and I can't get out of the place at all unless Mr. Jacobs chooses to unlock the gates and somebody goes with me to see that I don't run away. They say, Lord Rodono says, that

Carlton House is a lodge in a garden of cucumbers compared with ours, and grandmamma says, 'Very probably.' She calls the royal family 'a horde of Germans,'
and says that they eat sausages in the Throne Room.
She thinks that very bad, but I see no advantage in being
a prince unless you can do as you please—and if you like
sausages, why not eat them where you can? We are to
go there on Wednesday week, so I shall be able to judge.
I shall certainly eat sausages if I'm asked. Dick likes all
this parade, or says he does. It makes me think of dear
papa, who taught mamma to run away from it, and I cry
my eyes out at night sometimes when I know there won't
be a footman there to hand a handkerchief or catch my
tears in a bottle. Truly, that's the *only* time I am alone."

She has something more to say of Mrs. Moth, her new
maid.

"Grandmamma has sent away poor Gibson—there was
such a scene! The dear girl sobbed and clung, vowed
she'd be cut off me in pieces; but 'her ladyship' was not
to be moved, so she went yesterday, and now I'm without
a friend in England. I'm glad to say that she has gone
to her old aunt's at Plashetts—Cousin George Coigne's
place in Hertfordshire—and I'm promised faithfully to
see her once a year. 'Moth' is the name of my new maid
—like a person's in Shakespeare! Mrs. Moth. She is
a very fashionable young lady, rather pretty, I suppose,
with quick black eyes, which she knows how to use, I can
see. She minces her words, calls china *chaney*, and me

Miss *Cheembre*. You should have seen her picking over my clothes, raking about with finger and thumb. She and grandmamma fingered them together, and bickered over them like two hoodie crows. I was furious, but it made no difference. Madame Pelerine, or some name of the sort, was sent for to make me 'fit to be seen'—that will take half-a-dozen gowns at least, according to Moth. If they are to be like some I saw at Lady Jersey's last night I shall die of shame. My sweet cousin, you never saw such gowns, or such absence of gowns—literally *abandoned!* Mrs. Fancourt was there, like Venus rising from the sea—happily somewhere near the waist she thought better of it, and the rest remained under muslin. As for Lady Oxford—but my pen refuses its office—*burns my hand*."

It is at about this time that we meet with her in some of the gossips, diarists of the time. Lady Susan C—, who had known her in Ireland, writing to the Duchess of L—, "I met Hermy Chambre at D— House, the dear sweet. She was looking lovely—radiant—with her hair done up *à la Grecque*, and her beautiful shoulders slipping in and out of her bodice. Her roses put us wicked old Cockneys to shame. She has a very bold way of speaking, I must say—she always had—and will give Lady M. some trouble, I doubt. I hope she will. That's a proud old mouse-trap of a woman, my dear soul. . . ." Mervyn Touchett, too, was greatly taken with her. . . . "2d February. Dined at Caryll House—a large party—

Sussexes, Badlesmeres, Crowlands, Rogers, of course, Lady Embercourt, Moira and his *flame*, Hertford, without his, &c., &c. The *débutante* was in fine *verve*, coloured like a ripe peach—melting ripe, M. said: a charming as well as a lovely person. Prinny is said by Tom C— to be mightily struck, and she is quite to his taste: beautiful! She has wit, or, rather, raillery, but can be seriously scornful when she chooses. We talked politics —old Stanhope's *perpetual motion* about the State of the Nation, condition of the people, and what-not. She said that we talked of England as though it were a 'gentleman's seat,' and the people the rabbits in it. Why did we always treat 'the people' *en bloc* like a head of game? I replied that Bonaparte had made us think in continents, but that you always heard of a man, however obscure, when he was hanged. 'Yes,' says Miss, raising her fine brows, 'we're all noble when we're dead— all peers then.' Not much in it, of course, but she intended to snub me—and did."

Here you have her, then, as a strong young swimmer breasting the current of London's tide. "I have seen," she writes, "Lord Crowland, Saint Paul's, Westminster Abbey, the lion at Exeter Change, and Madame Catalani. I put them in the order of their coming, though it is that of my appreciation too. Lord Crowland is strikingly handsome. Do you know the story of his marriage? It is most romantic. He had loved her for *years*, though she was the wife of another, and finally, when they were travelling abroad somewhere, his feelings overcame him, and he spoke to her. She confessed the state of her heart, and they have been married quite a long time. . . . There was a divorce, naturally, and I believe a meeting between the gentlemen. I have seen her, too; she was very kind to me. I think *him* cold, and, though you may not agree, extremely *correct*. Of course, he is a chief of the Whig clan, which Lord Rodono calls *plus royaliste que le roy*, because it considers itself to be king of kings. Lord R. is in the House of Commons, and pretends to be a *Jacobin;* but Captain Ranald—Lord Clanranald's son and a real hero—says that he's nothing of the sort. I am great friends with both of these personages. Mr. Ranald is the bravest man that ever lived since papa and Lord Edward died; he is a sailor and, Lord Rodono says, a pirate. He uses very strong language—hates the Government. He says that nothing can be done *without pikes.*"

She goes about, here to a great house, there to a great assembly—to Almack's, for instance—wondering, watching, judging out of her young clear eyes. She is taken to Court, and kisses the old Queen's hand, and even there can find a moment in which to pity "the poor, faded, kind princesses." She is at Carlton House, kissed by the Prince of Wales. . . . "He was sadly flushed, Mary, and smelt of brandy ; but you could see the ravages of beauty in him—his eyes, for instance, are extraordinary, bright blue, and not cold, but hot and impetuous, like that

young butcher's I told you about, who fought two gentlemen at once—and I must say that he was charming. He
talked to me, standing, for ten minutes at least, neglect-
ing a whole herd of people who were waiting to kiss or to
be kissed, and then led me into another room and sat by
me on a divan. Grandmamma came, too, of course—she
never lets me out of her sight (as if I were a jewel-case on
a journey!)—but he hardly noticed her. He talked for
nearly half an hour, I suppose, and if I could believe a
word he said I should call him a perfect *Jacobin*. He
might lead England to liberty, Mary, if he chose! He
said that he had loved Lord Edward like a blood-brother,
and that he loved papa for being on his side. But he
owned that, situated as he was with the King and Ministers, he could do nothing—as yet. Some day, he said, he
hoped and prayed might see him King of the *English*,
not of England, which 'nobody,' he said, most impres-
sively, 'has ever been since the death of King Edward the
Confessor, my revered ancestor.' This may have been
blarney, my dear, to suit my Irish upbringing, but it was
very beautiful, and made grandmamma snort. I own
that it made me near crying. Then the rather disagreeable but most witty Mr. Sheridan came up, and said something in a low voice, and the Prince kissed my hand before he went off with him. Mr. Sheridan's eyes are burning black. Grandmamma was very gracious as we drove
home—said I had had a great success. . . . "

All very pleasant so far; but a week later we get a taste

of her quality, where it conflicts with my Lady Morfa's. I dare not omit it.

"I have had a passage of arms with grandmamma," she tells her Mary Fox, "rather unpleasant while it lasted, but I got my way. It was all about Harriet Moon, who is her companion and secretary, it seems, though I never knew it before. Well, the day before yesterday, when I came upstairs after luncheon, I found a girl standing, bonneted and pelissed, in the corridor leading to grandmamma's wing—as if she was waiting for somebody. I hardly glanced at her, but just noticed that she looked thin and pale, and had mournful eyes, very large— brown, I thought them, and so they are, beautiful eyes indeed. I read for an hour, and then Moth came to dress me for a drive—and when I went down, there was the girl still standing in the corridor. I asked her, Did she want anything? And she thanked me very nicely, and said, 'Oh, no.' So I drove until it was dusk, and then came back and went upstairs—and there was that poor girl still standing! This time I asked her if she would not come in and rest in my sitting-room by the fire; and she refused for a long time. But I insisted, and she began to cry—so I settled it by leading her bodily in. I put her by the fire with her toes on the fender, and sent Moth down to get her some cake and a glass of wine— for she looked *famished*.

"The wine revived her. I was as kind to her as I could be, and made her tell me everything. She was Harriet

Moon, she told me, who had been to her people in Shropshire—nursing her mother, I think—and had over-stayed her leave by two or three days. And this, if you please, was 'her ladyship's' way of showing her high dis-pleasure—to keep that miserable girl, after two days and a night in the stage-coach, waiting in the corridor from half-past one to half-past four, without bite or sup. Apart from the savagery of the revenge, apart from the hatefulness of stooping so far for vengeance, think of the terror of that shivering wretch, who dared not move even when the tyrant was out! It gave me a horror, but made my cheeks burn like fire. I do so *detest* power used like that.

"Well, Harriet Moon was in a terrible fright as to what 'her ladyship' would say or do when she found out what I had done; and, as it happened, her own woman did come in presently to say that 'Miss Moon was wanted!' I sent a message to say where she was, and that she would come; and then, as the timid creature was quite white and trembling, I decided to go with her. And I did it—took her arm, and marched into grandmamma's boudoir as bold as you please. I said, 'Grandmamma, I've brought Miss Moon to you, but you mustn't tease her to-night. You've made her quite ill enough as it is. I think you've been most unkind—and if you are going to be cross with her, I shall punish you.' Of course, I made her think that this was said for impudence, but I meant it. I had a plan—what do you think? I had made up my mind that, unless she was pleasant to the girl, I should threaten to tell the Prince the whole story!

"Grandmamma's head began to shake, as it always does when she's put out; she shook like a poplar leaf when I told her about the staked horse and the fight at the gates—and she wagged her hand about on her crutch. I could see that she was very vexed with me, but she pretended that she hadn't known Miss Moon was there. She calls her 'Moon'—did you ever hear such arrogance? She told me to go away, but I said that I could not until she understood that I had insisted on taking Miss Harriet into my room, &c., &c. And then I went on to talk about all sorts of things, 'in my airy way,' as Cousin George Fox calls it, and made her laugh. That ended it. Harriet came to me late that same night, after I had returned from Almack's, and thanked me. She has pretty ways, and lovely brown eyes—quite lovely. I think she's *cowed* here, and driven to various concealments and subterfuges, poor, pretty creature. She is two or three years older than I am, but has the spirit of a mouse. The whole affair has made an impression upon me. It is very hateful, I think. How furious my dear papa would have been. I saw him really angry once over some such cold piece of cruelty. 'If you stoop, Hermy,' he said to me once, 'stoop nobly.' "

Miss Chambre seems here to have begun her championing of the oppressed, and she continued it long. She is to continue it, I tell you fairly, until this book is done, in various ways and by divers expenditures of person, name, and fame. She is to retire from the fray—I scorn concealment; leave that to poor Miss Moon—sane and whole, but not without bruises. Bruises are to be looked for, unless you follow the practice of Hippolyta, Queen of the Amazons. She and her virgin cohorts, we know, maimed themselves before battle. Miss Hermia Mary never stopped for that.

The note deepens from this point, the letters cry. Here is one extract, torn from the girl's heart: "Behind all this enormous parade I seem now and then to be guessing, groping after monstrous shapes which evade me— an indifference, an ignorance, a callousness to rights, sufferings, private torture, which almost pass belief. I'll tell you more later, when I know more; just now my heart is on fire. Love me, Mary, love me still, before I am past all loving, and nothing but a silver-papered parcel on a high shelf in a cabinet. Now and till then, your Hermy."

Here is a "p.p.s.," with a comic wistfulness in it—serio-comic, as I believe. . . . "I have seen the place in the wall of the garden over which mamma climbed when dear papa came for her. His horse stood immediately below, in the park. The iron spikes, which he broke off, have never been replaced. I see a glimmer of hope through the gap." Now comes a break of more than a week, and then a real cry of pain. The girl is shocked. . . .

"Oh, Mary! Oh, Mary! I can hardly write for

shame. You remember what I told you of the scene outside the gates—of the murdered horse? You'll never believe me. Those two young men were my Uncle Morfa
and his friend, Lord Edlogan. This is literally true.
They now own to it. They were tipsy, but that is no
excuse for what is going on now. They have sent the
owner of the horse to prison, and mean to keep him
there without a trial. He's a Radical, I hear. I can't
tell you any more just yet.—Your disgraced HERMIA
MARY."

CHAPTER V

SO we are back again, dead-up against the butcher's horse, and that combat about his carcase which had so discouraged Miss Hermia Mary, and over which the eagle-beaked Countess of Morfa, blinking her little angry, intolerable eyes, had proposed to herself to take a soaring flight. The facts were perfectly simple. The gentlemen had been lunching, the person had been grossly impudent—what more need be said? And at least let nothing whatever be said to an ardent Miss Chambre unstrung by travel. And nothing was said—and yet the affair was not laid. To treat it as though it had never been proved a counsel of perfection, with circumstances fatally against it; for first Lord Morfa, a sickly youth, fell ill, as we know, and kept his bed, and next Lord Edlogan, his friend—Beauty Edlogan they called him, and Marquis of Edlogan he was, the Duke of Wentsland's son—discovered an inflammation of the nose; and, thirdly, the butcher was taken to the King's Bench, and lay there awaiting his charge. Lastly, the worst of all, politicians settled down in clouds, and the various wounds began to fester—and then Lady Morfa lost her temper, and determined not to charge the butcher at all, but to keep him where he was. By degrees and degrees, the facts obtruded themselves, by degrees took shape and got themselves in motion, until at last all London seemed to be swirling round a maelström-gulf, at bottom of which you might, if you had had a head to look with, have discerned the mangled remains of a horse. Round and round, nearer and nearer in, swirled our actors and a hundred more; and some of them were sucked down and had to battle for dear life to win the free air again, and some went under, heels first, and were known no more—and all because a tipsy gentleman staked a butcher's—? Not at all, but because Family came into conflict with the Mob, and out of the Mob a head uplifted and discovered itself to be that of a person, not to be treated *en bloc*, like rabbits in a park. It is a sign of the breaking-up of things old when the Mob—that *colluvies*—segregates into persons with souls to be lost or won. There's the significant thing for us—that the age as we know it was yeasting in the bowl. But let us take the facts of the case, as Miss Chambre got them out, and see how simple they may have been.

The facts were that Lord Morfa and his friend Edlogan, after a generous meal together, were about to enter the curricle of the first and proceed to the park, when they saw the famous horse tethered to the railings, and with that eye for a fine young animal which nobody of their acquaintance could refuse them, they admired. They did more; they examined it point by point, and became inflamed by its perfections. They were touched, they were pricked in their honour, they were affronted. Damn the fellow, where did he get such a horse, a blood horse, a pacer? Put a saddle, which you could call a saddle, on that horse, and a man might air him in the Row. One had seen a fellow on a worse horse in Pall Mall, and taken no notice. It was a start, a rummy go—whose was the horse? Jacob Jacobs, his gates open, touched his hat at this point. It was young Vernour's, the butcher's, my lords. The butcher's! Damn the butcher—this was no horse for him. Lord Morfa's offended eyes interrogated those of his friend. What the deuce were we coming to? he required to know.

Edlogan briskly said that he must try the horse—and did. Round and about he cantered, to the admiration of all. A perfect action, a great goer! The horse had a mouth. Morfa, who was undoubtedly drunk—everybody admitted that—and when drunk very mettlesome, was now for putting him at the railings round the grass-plat. This kind of horse, he told Edlogan—Irish, he would swear—could jump like a cat. Would Edlogan bet upon it? Damn it, a man should back his opinion, hey? And here Jacob Jacobs, finding himself under the enquiry of his master, again touched his hat and said, "Certainly, my lord." He blamed himself for that afterwards. The carriage-drive, you must know, formed a great circle of grit, and in the midst had an enclosure

of grass, round about the statue of the prescient Earl
Rupert, fenced in by stout iron rails not more than five
feet high—close rails, as sharp as spears.

Lord Edlogan, who owned to having been fresh, but
denied that he had been drunk, had laughed his friend
to scorn. "You'll cut his head off, Roddy, and break
your neck—sure as a gun you will. You've a bad seat at
the best, my boy, but when you're drunk you've no seat
at all," and so on; whereat, and at jeers from beyond
the gates, possibly also on a view of the concerned eyes
of Jacob Jacobs, anxious for the welfare of a peer, Lord
Morfa grew hot. Damn the horse! damn Edlogan! he'd
show what could be done. He flung his caped overcoat
to the gate-keeper, and, after a brief but glorious
struggle, was able to mount the nervous little animal.
He gave him a couple of smacks on the flank with his
glove, pushed him with his knees, dug his heels in
sharply, and went round the gravel court at an easy canter, which he increased to a sort of a gallop as the mur-
murs from the gates struck his ears. Jacob Jacobs had
got back to his post, lest the mob should invade the
sanctuary, "and God knows what next," as he put it.
From there he saw, and quaked to see, my lord take a
couple of turns, rocking dangerously in his seat; "and
the daylight you could see betwixt his lordship's fork and
the saddle would have mended a Sunday afternoon," said
he. But the madness of high blood! After that turn or
two about and about, all of a sudden "his lordship took

and screwed the hoss's head round, and in with his heels ;
and he put him at the rails *with a short rein,* did his lordship." Words failed him here to describe the queer
silence that followed, as the gallant little beast did his
gallantest. But the run was absurd, the take-off next to
nothing. He swerved as he refused, and disposed of his
rider ; but then, as if startled by the howls of the audience
he had, he gathered his legs under him and tried the
fence. There was no howling now—it was too horrible
—nameless. Indeed, though he lashed himself free, it
was but to die—and at that moment of glazing eyes the
butcher came out from the shrubbery which concealed the
tradesman's door. Lord Morfa was by that time at the
great gates, very shaky, tense and white, being helped
into his overcoat of many capes by his servitor, and
Edlogan, half crying with excitement and honest grief,
was standing by him, adjuring him "for God's sake" to
get out of this. The mob was distracted for the moment
by watching what the horse's owner would do.

His name was Vernour, David Vernour ; he was the
"son" of Vernour and Son, family butchers, of Brook
Street, Hanover Square. He was a fine young man,
broad-breasted, tall, and well-made ; he may have been
five or six-and-twenty. He was of the Saxon type, blue-
eyed, fair-haired ; one who flushed easily and had not
much to say for himself. Yet it came out afterwards
that he was "superior," and something of a public
speaker—also that he was a Radical—but even Tories

might have done what he did. His friends averred that he did not know Lord Morfa by sight, but most of them were constrained to add that, had he known him, it would have made no difference to his conduct. He was admittedly hot-tempered.

At first he grew very red, and ran forward to the fallen horse, knelt by it and put his cheek to its nostrils. It was still alive then, but breathing faintly; it lay in a pool of bright blood—arterial blood. With "a kind of sob," as it was afterwards told to Miss Chambre (and no harm done to his case), he bent his head over his horse —then threw it up, and stiffened at the shoulders as he looked over to the gates to find out with whom he must reckon. He seemed to decide quickly, for he rose to his feet and strode over the gravel; and he must have been beside himself when he, bare-headed, in his blue frock and apron, could clip the young Marquis of Edlogan on the shoulder, and bring him sharply round as if he had been stung. Good heavens! and had he not been stung?

"Who did that?" Jacob Jacobs would swear that he never said "my lord." He never used the word "lord," and only once said "sir." He might have been talking to any common person.

Edlogan, not liking his tone, which was curt, nor, perhaps, his question, which was to the point, replied, "Couldn't say, my man," and turned his back. It is supposed that he meant to be loyal to his friend—and, at any rate, he had not done it. Whereupon Vernour rounded on Lord Morfa with his "Is that your work, sir?" He was more respectful now, and all might yet have been well had not the mob answered the question.

" 'Twas my lord as done it. That's your man, butcher," and so on.

Morfa never looked at him at all; he swore at large. "Damn it all," said he, "it was the ——— horse's fault, and this ——— mob here."

"I left the horse tethered to the railings," says Vernour, and Lord Morfa jumped about.

"Who the hell are you? I wish you'd go to the devil," he snapped at him.

"If I do that," said Vernour, "I take you with me;" and with that he scruffed the young peer with so firm a grip that nothing in the power of Edlogan, no adjuration from the shocked lips of Jacob Jacobs—whose "For the Lord's sake, Vernour, for the Lord of Mercy's sake loose my lord!" should have been double-edged—would induce him to let go. Lord Morfa, not a cleanly young man, used atrocious language; Lord Edlogan stormed and argued, was heartily ashamed of the whole affair, and the more ashamed he was the more angry he got. "The fellow was unreasonable," he afterwards explained. "He'd have been paid, of course—I'd have paid him if Roddy wouldn't—and I know Roddy don't like to part— but, damn it! he had him like a rag-doll—and a man can't stand that." Moved by such feelings, he certainly attacked Vernour—and with spirit; the crowd swarmed

and serried for the fight; a chimney-sweeper and an un-
shaven man with no voice whatsoever formed and kept a
ring. Vernour, with but one hand free, stopped Edlogan's rushes; and as the great Caryll chariot came
rumbling in had just sent him on to his back. In the
breathing pause which he obtained his eyes, fierce with
battle, met those of Miss Hermia Chambre, dwelt on
them, and were dwelt upon. The carriage rolled on, the
mob surged and serried; and Jacob Jacobs, powerless to
serve his gods, fled wailing for the constables.

Upon their arrival, David Vernour released his limp
victim and went quietly to the King's Bench. That is the
truth of this very disagreeable affair, which her ladyship
wished to ignore, but could not.

CHAPTER VI

LORD MORFA had kept his room for some days,
and the house his counsel—so well that uncle and
niece met, when at last they did meet, in very friendly
fashion. Miss Chambre had not the least suspicion that
the slight, pale, black-haired, dark-chinned, and suffering
young man in a dressing-gown of preposterous elegance
had recently been under her eyes swinging like a dead
cat in the hold of the flushed butcher. Searching, as she
was fond of doing, for character, she seemed to find it
in his laconic manner. She liked his "How do, Hermy?"
and two fingers from the sofa, and returned him a cheerful "Quite well, thank you, Uncle Morfa," with a stoop
downwards, and a fresh cheek to touch his own. She was
sorry for the fevered youth, had felt his cheek to be dry
and hot, was very ready to excuse his irritability with his
mother and his valet, and set herself to work to smooth
out his "creases," as she called them.

There was plenty to say: apart from the coach at Holy-
head and Mr. Aloysius Banks, who were ancient history
by this time, there were the new conjuror, the Prince of
Wales, and Madame Catalani singing "God shave the

King." Lord Morfa, who liked women, liked them to be
pretty, vivacious, and, above all, plump—"well covered,"
as he put it—was certainly amused. He lay back on his
cushion, his hands behind his head, and fixed her with
his fever-bright eyes. "Good gel—that's capital!
Egad, ma'am, I must keep that for Prinny—oh, he'll be
a proud man, by George!" He was certainly pleased
—and so her tongue ran on. "And oh, Uncle Morfa, I
quite forgot to tell you. As we came in—that first day
—there was a fight. . . . " Lady Morfa called sharply,
"Curtis," and sent the valet to see if the carriage were at
the door. . . . His lordship moved uneasily, but did not
turn his eyes away, or cease to smile.

"Yes, a real fight—at the gates. . . . "

"Dessay," said his lordship. "They *will* fight, Hermy,
when they're drunk, you know."

"And they were drunk," said she. "Two of them were;
but one was not. He was a hero, I thought."

"They fight, you know," he said dreamily, "like the
very devil." So he got her off the line.

"But he does it without being drunk. . . . "

"*Ex officio*," said Lady Morfa; and then, "Come, child,
or you'll tire the invalid."

She rose and looked benevolently down upon her victim.
"They took a fine vengeance upon the man who wasn't
tipsy," she said. "They sent him to prison for it."

"Dessay," said Lord Morfa; "where the devil's my
man? Look here, I shall go to sleep, I think." She

stooped and touched his forehead. "Poor Uncle Morfa!" she said kindly, and went away with her grand-mamma to a party.

And then she forgot the thing, left it, perhaps, em-balmed in the recesses of her mind—why, how should she remember it between drastic inspections of gowns by her ladyship, visits to Madame Pelerine, visits to Saint Paul's, Lord Crowland's romantic person, Lady Ox-ford's display of charms? Never was such a whirl as hers—and we were all whirling at once like a set of jug-gler's tops. Dick must go to the *levée*, she to Bucking-ham House; Carlton House to follow; a dinner to meet the Prince; Wednesday the opera; Thursday a dinner and a rout; Friday the Duchess's ball—and so forth. She made her little sensation, she was admired, and she knew it. Let heroes languish in chains in the King's Bench, let Harriet Moon shiver in corridors—but she, the young beauty, would float from rout to rout, and gather her roses, and give them away.

Mervyn Touchett saw her at R— House. "Saw the little Caryll heiress holding her court. Sedate and glow-ing on a divan, half-a-dozen bucks round about her. Stout men, too—politicians, Tierney, Tom Rodono, Wormwood, and Bob Ranald, very brisk. She waltzed and looked sumptuous." The waltz was stark new that year. . . . "My dear, I have been in a dozen men's arms!" this to Mary Fox. "I'm hot all over. But every-body does it now." In far Kilbride, where nobody did it, Mary Fox felt worried. There were more serious things to worry about, if she had but known.

They say that she was a "man's woman"; and she confesses somewhere that she preferred men's society. . . . "The women, Mary, rather horrify me. They preen themselves like pigeons in the sun—and sit apart as if they were in a slave-market. As for the girls, they are dolls; dolls with palpitations!" She seems to have had a singularly quick judgment, and to have acted upon it without faltering, to have known instantly when she could afford to be frank. She had decided at a glance that she liked Harriet Moon; and when she met Captain Ranald at a dinner-party, though she had never seen him before, she did not scruple to tell him that she was a rebel in grain, almost before he had time to inform her that he was a Jacobin.

Captain the Hon. Robert Ranald, a gallant, brick-coloured, fiery-haired little seaman, whose acts in the high seas, in the mouths of French rivers and in broken Atlantic roadsteads form a Saga, was at this time in England, persecuting the Ministry in the name of common-sense. He was now one of the members for Westminster, and overweeningly popular with the mob. As he was quite without virulence or prejudice, he was detested by the Government, which had both in abundance. They battered him, and made him laugh; he hammered them, and they were vowed to his ruin. Mr. Croker, it was said, would cheerfully dance at Carlton House for Bob

Ranald's head upon a charger. This spoke a volume for
the hero, who confessed himself an outlaw as he handed
Miss Chambre down to dinner.

"I'm home to stop thieving," he told her, "I'm in the
House to stop it, and every thief's hand is against me.
They don't like the facts, and they don't like me.   I
pound 'em; I go on pounding 'em; I bore 'em to death.
Burdett's far too much of a gentleman—besides, he does
'em the honour to disapprove of 'em.   He thinks 'em
villains, and I call 'em fools. So I'm half an outlaw in
the minds of Ministers, and half by my own showing.
If the fractions add themselves aright, Miss Chambre,
you have the arm of a man who must needs be hanged."

"I have held such arms before, sir," said she.   "Lord
Edward's was one, and my father's another."

They were seated by this, but Ranald, having looked
quickly at his companion, nevertheless got up and bowed
to her.   "You are Dick Chambre's daughter, and he was
Fitzgerald's friend.   I'm happily mated."   He began to
speak of Ireland, and of Lord Edward, whom he
described as the bravest little gentleman and straightest
rider he had ever seen in his life.   But he was a fool, unhappily, because he let those qualities rule his politics.
"You can be too brave—you can be too true to the scent.
The pace may kill or the field desert you: you die a
lonely death.   But in my opinion it is better to die in
Newgate with Fitzgerald than to reign with Castlereagh
in Pall Mall.   The little man was a hero, and a Saint."

Her cheeks flushed, her eyes were dewy. "A divine fool —that is what I know. Everybody must know it in time. I can't speak of him without tears—" And then, with a catch in her voice, "My father was just like that."

"Not a doubt of it," he said. "He rode straight and rode hard. But, as you know, and I know, he didn't ride hard enough for the Castle in '98."

"He broke his horse's heart," said Hermia Mary, "and couldn't get another. . . . You never knew my father?" He folded his arms, considered them, and his reply. Then he looked her in the face.

"I know more of him now than I ever did before. I know that he must have broken his own heart as well." Miss Chambre was unable to reply.

Her neighbour of the right-hand was Lord Rodono, a cheerful, fresh-faced nobleman, eldest son of the Earl of Drem. He was tall, upright, stoutly built, sanguine of complexion, was in Parliament for an obscure burgh, a great admirer of women, and very much esteemed by most of them. His somewhat cold, critical blue eyes, perhaps, gave confidence; his care not to commit himself certainly did. In politics he ranked with the opposition, as became the heir of Drem; but he dallied, never indiscreetly, with the reformers. Like every man born he talked of himself, and found himself the best joke in the world. He told Miss Chambre that he liked Whig women, but went among the Jacobins for male society. There were, in truth, no male Whigs—that was a contradition in terms. A man goes by passion, a woman by feelings. Now you can passionately decree that somebody should wear a gold hat, or passionately attempt to knock that off his head: that is as a man is Tory or Radical. "But no man of my acquaintance," he said, "will choose to crown his fellow with straw, and then insist that it's every bit as good as gold—in fact, much better, because it's the same thing, only cheaper. For that charming fantasy we look to your sex, Miss Chambre."

"But you are a Whig, Lord Rodono? You crown the King with straw."

"Pardon me, madam, I am a servant of Whigs," he said, with a bow, which she felt to be too pronounced.

She avowed herself a Jacobin, and he applauded the confession. A pike would become her; Bob Ranald was all for pikes. He questioned, however, her grandmamma's view. The peerage impaled—eh?

"Grandmamma has never talked politics to me," said Hermia; but Lord Rodono was looking at the venerable lady, who sat upon their host's right-hand, and was talking of Mr. Clark, that Cytherea of the mart. Thus it was that the cat came out of the bag.

"How under the eyes of heaven she allowed you to be entrusted to Bob Ranald," he said musingly, "passes belief. She thinks him poisonous, she calls him 'unfortunate.' Now that's nonsense, of course—poor Bob's as wholesome as a March gale; but he's not judicial—he thinks with his heart. He's gone red-hot into that affair of yours."

"What affair of mine?" she asked, thinking more of Ranald, whom she admired, than of herself.

"Oh, the butcher's horse, you know." His eyes twinkled with friendly malice, and seemed to have their reward. He brought her round in a flash.

"My affair, Lord Rodono! Indeed, it was no affair of mine. It was very hateful."

"I beg your pardon. I meant of your family's. Your grandmother's—Roddy's affair. And then there was Edlogan's nose—that was in it, too. Very awkward business indeed. Now Bob Ranald——"

But Miss Chambre was now moved in earnest—she was flooded with colour. "Uncle Morfa! Lord Edlogan! Do you—can you mean that they—?" She made him stare.

"Good God, didn't you know that? Why, it's all over town. Now I've put my foot in it."

He certainly had, as far as she was concerned, for she had nothing more to say to him. She was really scandalised, but she was startled also—shocked, alarmed. Her feelings were tumultuous—why had this been hidden from her? What was going on? Of what sort were these smooth-voiced, courteous people she was among? Flesh and blood? Her flesh and blood? To grind the faces of the poor—and to smile, and bow, and be witty—and enormously at ease—served on bent knees! That was a veritable cry of the heart when she said, "Oh, Lord Rodono, that cannot be true!"

He had to assure her that it was true, and to make out a case. "The man attacked Roddy before he'd heard what there was to say. Nothing much to say, I grant you—but no doubt he'd have been paid, not the slightest doubt. And, of course, he *will* be paid in the end—if politics are kept out of it. But he's known to Ministers as a speaker in the Forum, and those sort of places—Crown and Anchor, and all that; and he attacked a smaller man in his own place—and the constables were fetched, as they ought to have been. They did the rest; the rest was not Roddy's doing—Roddy was abed. I think that you'll find it will all settle down—unless Bob Ranald makes a hash of it. And, as I tell Roddy, he must keep Sandgate from hearing of it." Such talk as this had no effect on her at all; she was quick enough to see that the speaker was extenuating, making smiling apologies, as it were, for shutting the prison-doors. "Really, if there's going to be all this to-do—if you'll allow me, I'll just—I feel myself in need of repose!" She grew hot all over as she felt the spiked walls of Caryll House closing in upon her, and, in her mind's eye, saw Jacob Jacobs in his gold-laced hat and shoulder-knots, sorrow upon his face, locking the great gates. Hateful thought—and she the daughter of Dick of the Gallop! And she who had stood open-armed, warm-bosomed to England! And this was England! And those proud eyes of the strong fighter

—she remembered them now—were to be purblinded in the dark—while the Carylls smiled at ease! Angry, indignant, sore, alarmed, the *débutante* looked fiercely about her world.

"Forgive me"—this was Ranald's voice—"I heard Rodono talking. It's true, what he said of me. I am not judicious. I believe I'm glad of it. If every one were judicious, justice would never be done. I know Vernour, and intend to help him—indeed, I'm bound to that, for he's in my constituency. He's a Westminster freeman, and a fine fellow. No offence to you."

"Offence—no, no!" She was fingering breadcrumbs, looked very uncomfortable—but raised her fine eyes to his. "Captain Ranald, I must not talk about it—now—now that I know—" She couldn't finish; and then he spoke vehemently to her, but under his breath.

"This place—this country—London, England—is not fit for the likes of you to inhabit. A rat-pit of a country! Who dares be honest? Who can afford it? Privilege, privilege, privilege! There's the sound of your horse's hoofs—and down goes young Vernour. I should like to tell you about him—some day."

She blushed, but she said, "Tell me now." But he would not say much.

"When I'm free to speak—when I've got him out. I'll tell you this, though: he's the last man in the world to be served in this way, because he's sensitive. He's quick. He feels himself strong—and that kind get dashed, and hurt themselves. They kick at the pricks—and injustice, or what's worse, indifference, bites inwards and corrodes. They may poison the man through before they've done with him. But there! he's Mob—and you're Family—and justice must be done, God save us! And they wonder that I'm a reformer—and say that I wield a muck-rake. Well, you must!"

She was regarding him now so earnestly, was so absorbed that he checked himself. "Let me advise you, keep out of this affair. You can do nothing, absolutely nothing. Nobody can do much but patch-work. We have to fight with unhallowed swords. You—if you ever come into battle—must come like Joan of Arc, with a sword pure from the altar. I'll follow you then. Ah, you are going? Good-bye."

The ladies rose. Hermia took her place with the procession, but, as if by intention, her grandmother waited for her, took her hand, and led her from the room. He saw the girl blush, bite her lip, lower her eyes.

"All your troubles before you, my dear," he said to himself. "She'll get mauled, but she'll come out somehow." Then he helped himself to the claret.

CHAPTER VII

THAT dinner-party had been in the second week of February, at which time also we must place that crying letter of Miss Chambre's to Mary Fox—the "Love me, Mary, love me still" letter—as I suspect; and that other which records the disgraceful truth. Why, being the girl we know her, she did not "have it out" with old Lady Morfa has now to be explained. She had already had a passage of arms with her, the reader will recollect, over the cowering form of Miss Harriet Moon, and had been victorious in that encounter. Here she had a stronger case, and was herself the stronger for victory; and yet she contented herself with outpourings to a Mary Fox!

Well, first of all, she had to make sure of her ground; she had to find out the whole of the story as we know it now. She must interrogate Jacob Jacobs, Progers, a housemaid who had seen the tragedy from an attic window; she must learn that his lordship had been tipsy, and his language "very free." She must find out from Bob Ranald what he had at first withheld, that David Vernour was an exceptional butcher—a politician who was welcome at Wimbledon, a strong speaker, a

superior young man. He had taught himself French, to
read Rousseau, Latin, "to break his teeth on Livy."
The Government was said to have an eye on him, and this
case of his imprisonment was interesting Cobbett. A
"man called Hazlitt" was said to be foaming at the
mouth on his account at Winterslow, in Wilts, and Lord
Sandgate, a vehement nobleman, was prepared to use him
as a flail for the Westminster threshing-floor, if he could
get no better. Ranald had communicated with the prisoner, had seen him twice, and had heard from him. He
showed Miss Chambre a letter from him, excellently
turned, firm in tone and full of spirit. She saw, in her
mind's eye, the young man writing that—saw the stiff
set of his head, the proud eyes of him which "look
through you and see that you are nothing." She was intensely interested, full of passion for justice—and yet
she did nothing. She did less than nothing: she was even
civil to Uncle Morfa, believing him a sorry little knave,
and meek to her grandmamma, who, she was sure, was a
wicked old woman. She went about as usual from ball
to ball, gathering tributes and dispensing smiles. Dinners to Princes of Wales, signal honours of an alcove,
dubious honours of Mr. Sheridan's black eyes, duchesses'
routs, compliments to her beauty, men of fashion, wits,
dandies, macaronis in circles or half circles about her
chair, boxes at the opera, hats off in the park, queen's
kisses, princesses's kisses—all done under the approving
eye of an old wolfish grandmamma who—and she knew it

now—had hated her father, scorned her mother, bullied a thin Harriet, and was deliberately keeping an injured man untried in gaol, and intended to keep him there! There were hours of the day, hours in the night, when Miss Chambre felt her cheeks on fire, and suffered such tumult at the heart that she knew not where to turn. How was this to be explained? Why did her heart beat, and why did she say nothing? The explanation is a simple one, and I am coming to it.

First of all, it had become certain that Vernour was to be kept in gaol, and not brought to trial until Caryll House chose. She gathered this beyond doubt by over-hearing grandmamma in talk with Uncle Morfa. It was in the library, a long room of many bays. She had come in for a book. Lord Morfa stood with his back to the fire; her ladyship, crutch in hand, was upright in a chair.

"Do nothing, Roddy."—This was the lady.—"Leave the matter in my hands. The man must be punished in the proper way."

"Very well, ma'am—only, mind you, I've told you what's going on. The Radicals have taken it up. Cobbett's at it, and Sandgate's asking questions in the House."

"That is excellent. The Ministers must answer them. No doubt the man's a Jacobin."

"No doubt at all," said Lord Morfa. "I happen to know he is."

"If anything more is said in the House, I'll see that Mr. Percival is properly instructed. You are ill—Lord Edlogan's ill: nothing can be done. Bail is out of the question."

"Well, I don't know, ma'am. Upon my honour——"

"Pardon me, Roddy, but I know perfectly well. I have been accustomed all my life to deal with persons of the sort."

Miss Hermia Mary left the library bookless, and in a tempest of feeling. Nothing she had ever heard of—not Lord Edward's death in Newgate—equalled the purposed tyranny of this. What would Captain Ranald say to it? What, alas! could he do but impotently rage, and appeal to a pitiless heaven? She paced the long corridors of Caryll House, ranged the suite of drawing-rooms, those famous yellow silk-damask rooms, mirrored, gilt-chaired, glassy-floored: she felt like a panther in a cage. Had her eye roamed that cedared garden and seen that gap in the wall of spikes it is not impossible that she would have fled the shameful scene. Luckily for herself she did not, but did, instead, a much more ordinary thing. She talked; girls must talk; and there was nobody but Harriet Moon. Talking to Harriet, she got a slap on the cheek—a tonic slap.

A thin and pale girl was this Harriet, with abundance of dark hair, a pathetic mouth, and the most pleading brown eyes you ever saw in your life. Bound hand and foot to Lady Morfa, she was a slave who did her best to

keep her soul alive in her body, but did it, as she was
forced, in furtive ways of her own which did not always
commend themselves to her new-found champion.   But
what little she had been able to win for herself she had
won by waiting for it; she was cautious, because she was
timid, and reticent in self-defence.   She was really
grateful to Hermia, and fond of her as far as she could
afford, but she would show neither gratitude nor affection until they were demanded of her.   Although she allowed herself to be kissed, and liked kissing as much as
anybody, she would never kiss back unless she was invited.   Perhaps she thought to enhance the value of her
kisses when they came by this means—but Miss Hermia
found that sort of thing a bore.   And so was it a great
bore that Harriet could hardly be forced to speak her
real mind.   The more of a mind she had the less easily
could she be forced.   She uttered herself like the personages of modern novels, ending her sentences with
dashes.

Interrogated, then, with passion upon the butcher's
wrongs and rights, she had a very scared look in her
brown eyes, and shrank visibly from committing herself
upon them.   But to direct questions of the Yes or No
order she had to reply that it was all quite true.   Her
ladyship did intend that Vernour should stop in prison;
bail was to be refused, and not a sixpence paid for the
horse—for the present.   How long could this go on?
She really hardly knew.   Her ladyship would decide when

the young man was sufficiently punished.   Punished!
Yes, Miss Chambre might be assured that punishment
was intended.

Miss Chambre found herself trembling in front of
Harriet.

"Are you sure of this?"

"Yes, Miss Chambre, quite sure."

"But—oh, heaven!   What's to be done?"

"I really could not say, Miss Chambre."

Hermia stamped her foot.   "You madden me with your
'Miss Chambres.'   Why, the man's horse was killed—
killed by Lord Morfa—*killed*, Harriet!"

Harriet's brown eyes were veiled by her fine,
curved lashes.   She coloured slightly—a suffusion
under the skin; no more.   "I have heard that it was
so."

"And do you tell me now that nothing is to be said of
that—no admission, no apology?"

"Apology!   Oh, no, indeed—none."   Harriet was now
bold enough to look at her flaming friend.   "Her ladyship is convinced of a plot—some political conspiracy
against the family.   I am sure she will do nothing now.
Her ladyship is very angry that any fuss has been made
—any notice taken at all.   Those things—publicity,
especially—always make her indignant."

Hermia shrugged her shoulders.   "I think grandmamma must be out of her senses.   I really do, Harriet.
She appears to believe that she can treat people worse

than cattle. I shall tell her so. I shall! Oh, Harriet,
what can I do?"

Harriet made very free. "If you please—if you will
excuse me——"

"Yes, yes, of course."

"I do hope that you will say nothing, do nothing at all.
Great harm would come of it. Her ladyship is peculiar,
and expresses herself—occasionally—" She succumbed
in confusion. Hermia opened her eyes wide.

"Expresses herself—! Why should she not? Do you
mean against me? Why not? What could she say, but
call me a little Jacobin, or tell me not to talk rubbish?
Do you think I should mind that?"

No—it evidently was not that; it was worse, much
worse. Harriet really could not bring herself to say
what it was; but of this she was sure, Miss Chambre would
rue the day when she spoke to her ladyship about Vernour's horse. If she had wished to be bayed like a hunted
stag, she had her desire; for now she was made to speak.

Holding her bosom, staring with her big eyes, she stam-
mered out her reading of Lady Morfa's mind. "Her
ladyship would say—oh, how can I tell you? I have no
right—I ought not! But I wish to save you—you have
been so good to me—Hermia! I may call you that!"
She was now in tears, so plainly distressed that it seemed
cruel to go on; but Hermia was unrelenting, though kind
about it.

"Please tell me what you mean, Harriet—and don't suppose that I shall misunderstand you. I am sure you mean me a service."

Miss Moon called heaven to witness the purity of her intentions, and with sobs proceeded. "Her ladyship would say—dear Hermia, forgive your friend—that the man was quite a common person, but that, of course, he was very handsome—and that you—that you had remarked upon that—and—that it was all very evident—" and hereupon she dissolved into a heap on the carpet.

Miss Chambre's most baffling quality was her simplicity. It was real simplicity; she read things as they were spelt. To this uncomfortable avowal of Harriet's, then, she replied with a fit of pondering, and the disconcerting admission, "Well, but he was handsome, remarkably so, I thought. And what, pray—?" but there she stopped in answer to a look from Harriet's eyes, directed at her from the floor—a look which she had never seen in any eyes before, an educated, experienced look—which she could read without any spelling at all, by the instinct which young women have and don't need to learn. And as she received this look, she started as if she had been whipped over the face—started and stared, and stood wondering, while the hot colour slowly tided over her, from the neck upwards to the roots of her hair. And then to her fierceness succeeded mildness; and then she turned and slowly left the room.

As for Harriet Moon, it is to be observed of her that she rose from the carpet, and for some time after her friend had left her walked the room in great agitation, with her arms crossed over her bosom, as if to hug her thought. Her sobbing had ceased, her eyes were bright, but not with tears. Occasionally she lifted them to heaven, or, let me say, the ceiling; and at such times her face wore the sort of expression one would look for in that of a virgin martyr.

CHAPTER VIII

A YOUNG, ardent, and pretty lady may decide that her grandmamma is a vulgar-minded old woman and rather horrible, and yet, almost in the same flash of indignation, clearly see that the less scope she offers to that vulgar mind the better for all concerned. Love of justice, to be sure, is a very fine thing, for the which one should gladly go through fire and water; but how when the fire is in the cheeks? How when it's the eyes that are to be drowned? It is a curious thing that the noblest passion of women is the one which they can least bear to have imputed.

When Miss Hermia Mary decided—as she did without knowing it—that the victim must languish in his chains so far as she was concerned, it cannot be denied that she was right. Burning cheeks, flames of indignation are a credit to a lady, and most becoming; but she must be sure that the fires are vestal, she cannot afford a hint against their honesty. Indeed, the moment that hint is possible, they cease to become honest; a hard saying, but so it is in this world. Now, at Harriet's interpretation of her grandmamma's mind, Miss Chambre had been first amazed, then scornful, then indignant; but at the discovery of her educated look, that piercing look of an intelligence beyond her own, she had blushed and been mild. She had come into conflict with something unsurmised, and it had quelled her. A seed of doubt had been sown in the garden-plot of her mind. Like Eve in another garden long ago, she could no longer be as she had been now that she knew herself. Like Eve in that garden of long ago, she ran sheltering into the brake, and made herself an apron of leaves.

I can't pretend to exhibit what is not to be seen. How can I say what her private mind was when the wild young creature, panic-struck, was cowering in covert? I don't suppose she dared think at all; but this much I know, that she was very conscious of changed relations with some of her little world; that, for once, she went in awe of her grandmother; that she was no longer anxious to hear Captain Ranald upon the superiority of Vernour; that she wished Lord Rodono to talk about himself; and that, on the other hand, she was drawn nearer to Miss Harriet Moon—to become friend rather than patroness. She did what she had never done in her life before—even with Mary Fox—she talked with Harriet of Lord Rodono's attentions, which were becoming marked, and of other allied topics. Love-affairs had been abstractions to her hitherto, the conventions of novelists and poets, about as pertinent to life as the blue roses and blood-red leaves upon the chintzes of your bed. But now you talked of them under your breath, and best in the twilight under the kindly flicker of the fire; now you became curiously interested; you wondered, you paused to wonder, and with a sigh gave over. And Harriet proved to be an expert; so Harriet grew. The change in Harriet herself, too, was very subtle; a little more decision, a good deal more ease. She was more demonstrative, she kissed more; sometimes she touched Hermia's cheek, a little stroking movement; and sometimes her arm would steal round Hermia's waist, and she would whisper. She was very discreet; there was no question of involving her friend in a common guilty secret; the change in her was very subtle, but it was there.

All this time—not a word to Mary Fox in Kilbride of the wrongs of Vernour and his murdered horse.

But there may have been another reason for that, since, about this end of February, there arose and spread over London a cloud of thick darkness which may well have swallowed up such troubles. A squalid romance, festering long in semi-secret, came to a head, and was rent. It poisoned the moral atmosphere; the soul sickened of that which it must breathe or die. What was Honour if a Duke of York could speak of it as his? What was Love if a Mary Ann Clark could enjoy it? What was the Justice worth whose ministers bandied quips with the criminal; and what Reform when its champions were leagued with a shameless merchant of herself? Stultifying questions which the cleanest had to ask themselves in that tainted London of February and March, when the town

could talk of nothing but Mr. Clark, the Rival Princes,
Colonel Wardle, and Lord Sandgate; when Throne,
Church, Legislature, and Executive alike uncovered
their sores, and there seemed no difference in corruption
between arraigners and arraigned. What wonder if a
young Eve, cowering in covert, was terrified out of her
new-bought knowledge of good and evil, when evil boasted
of its goodness, and goodness flaunted its core of evil?

In great Whig houses there was much appetite for the
offal cast up. The Whigs, like Pilate, had washed their
hands, and could afford to be merry at the expense of
of Princes and their bought loves. If the Duke had
bought Mrs. Clark, might she not buy the Duke? And
as for the Jacobins, exposing the precious pair, it was
not surprising that, *chemin faisant*, they should expose
themselves—bought also, in the very act of buying.
Old Lady Morfa and her friends bickered over the
affair like moulting eagles at a carrion, and spared
neither age nor sex the details of their feast. It was an
age of strong stomachs, but we must suppose that young
ones like our Miss Hermia were troubled with qualms.
Nothing of the sort could hinder Lady Morfa. She discussed the Duke of York and the Danaë of Gloucester
Place in season and out. She said of the Duke—Charles
Fitz-Payn reports it—that you could expect no less of
persons who could eat—and over-eat—in public than
that they should occasionally be sick in public; and for
her part, she failed to see that the relief was more dis-

gusting than the disease. This was said to Lord Crowland, who, whatever he may have thought of its taste, did
not choose to impugn its truth. But he was doubtful,
he said, whether the present deplorable penance was
remedial. "I don't attempt," he said, "to disguise from
you my opinion of the Exalted Personage—nor of all
such Personages. I think it a safe inference to draw,
that a king *may* be dangerous because he *must* be ridiculous. Now, if by House of Commons' pleasantries you
show him to be preposterous, the possible danger becomes a certainty."

But Lady Morfa scouted danger. "Dangerous! To
exhibit a poltroon! How can it be dangerous? Do we
not exist by maintaining it? We brought them in as
much for this kind of performance as for any other that
I can call to mind at the moment."

"Helot-kings," murmured Fitz-Payn, who had been
dining at the house. "Helot-kings, eh?"

"Precisely," said her ladyship, sipping her tea.
"Helot-kings sooner than helot-people. We foresaw
that in '89." She meant 1689, of course, the date of the
Redemption of Mankind.

Her son, the young Earl, not unconscious that he had
been playing helot-peer of late, took a less magisterial
view. Caryll House was "precious near" to Carlton
House in more senses than one; and how were the vexa-
tions of a Frederick of York going to affect the com-
forts of a George of Wales? Roderick of Morfa did

not disguise from his circle that his royal friend was unhappy. "Prinny is touched, ma'am," he said openly;
"he's badly hit—he'll take it hard."

Lord Rodono here observed that he was taking
it at Brighton; but the Earl had more anxieties to
consider.

"What," he cried, turning his suffering face to the
ceiling and the chandelier, "What's going to come to
Society, ma'am, if women of the town are to be asked
about? You'll find your Mrs. Clark at Lord B—'s and
Lord S—'s; you raise a thousand pound for your Ann
Taylor because she had a rip for a father and cried in
the witness-box. Damme, and what I say is this, where
are we going to be one of these days? We have our little
troubles, you know. We may have tears in the witness-
box before long. If they can harry a Prince of the
Blood, I s'pose they can harry a peer—eh?"

"Never," said Lady Morfa firmly; but her son was not
appeased.

"That's what Prinny says, ma'am. And Prinny's
right, as he always is—saving your presence."

"I think that His Royal Highness may leave our affairs to me," said Lady Morfa, with great decision, and
the conversation dropped by consent.

If the private sanctities of the most exalted persons are
to be outraged, if peers are to be flouted at their own
gates, where is the British Constitution, and how is that
to stand? You attack the Throne, you attack the House

of Lords; is there not a danger here? Do you not dislocate the Fabric? These were the questions put to Miss Chambre by her early acquaintance, Mr. Aloysius Banks, poet and flail of poets.

Mr. Banks, hovering on the brink of the great Clark affair and the allied topic of the butcher's horse, could not deny himself the privilege of instructing so lovely a being. Moreover, it had been at her intercession that a Norman house, one of the most guarded in London, had opened its great gates to him—not to dine, it's true, but to a party, to mingle familiarly with those who had dined. He felt a glow, and he exhaled it.

He pointed out that no number of private wrongs could justify a public wrong; that England was a great nation whose citadel had been reared by centuries of heroic suffering. The blood of the martyrs—let it flow, let it flow! Thus would the Constitution flourish. The body-politic, that wondrous harmony of King—Lords—Commons, must endure throughout the ages, cost what it might in the blood of beasts—he meant the butcher's horse—or the groans of stricken men—he meant the butcher. The Constitution was a lighthouse on a rock at sea, upholding the ray above tumult and riot. Men might drown on their floating spars, a ship might founder, and homes be desolate; but they of the House must feed the flame—their duty first and last. Let the appointed vestals—he meant Lords Morfa and Edlogan —see to it. Public opinion would support them, though faction should snarl—he meant the butcher—and grudge them service—he meant the butcher's horse.

Miss Chambre neither flushed nor paled, having opinions of her own upon these matters, and being patrician enough to ignore those of a Mr. Banks if they did not coincide. I think that she was never so inveterate a Caryll as when she played Jacobin. She had no intention of entering debate with Mr. Banks, and when Lord Rodono came up with a bow and a kiss for her hand, she rose, took his arm, and left the philosopher.

"Who's your mortified friend?" she was asked, and explained him, a critic who as good as owned to having slain a poet. Lord Rodono thought it very possible that he had also eaten him and found that he disagreed; and then he went on to speak of Vernour and his horse. That case was growing to be a scandal; here was March upon us, and no thought of a trial. It would end by making him a Radical, he said, and then he would move for a *Habeas Corpus*. "Cobbett's at it now," he told her, "and is going to be nasty. I'll tell you how I know that. He's speaking the truth."

"Do you mean that that is not his practice?"

"This is what I mean. When Cobbett has a bad case, he's not above improving it. He'll drag in the Orders in Council, or the Six Acts, or Smut in the Hops, or the Pension Lists—anything. But here he feels that he has a good one—too good to touch. I'll show you the *Register*—pretty strong writing. He gives the bare facts in twenty lines of print, and no more. I tell you it looks bad. There's to be a shindy. I feel it in the air."

Miss Chambre no longer faced him as of late—like the young Diana, as he had been pleased to think, as tense as her bowstring. She looked down at her foot tracing patterns on the carpet, and with her head thus hung asked him, What she ought to do?

The question flattered him, for he was falling in love; but he had nothing heroic to propose. "Whatever you do will do justice harm. You'll make it worse for the fellow; and you'll make the very mischief for yourself. Surely you see that? Motives will be imputed. Look at this infernal affair in the House. Do you see that man over there?" She looked in the direction intended, and saw a tall, thin, and pale gentleman with intensely black hair, and eyes like Mr. Sheridan's, who stood talking to nobody in the middle of the room. "That's Sandgate," he told her. "That's the fellow who doesn't understand that the Rights of Man won't do here. If he gets to know that you are at loggerheads with your family in this, Sandgate'll make a handle of you without mercy. He's a fanatic—he's dangerous because he's no scruples. He says that if you are for cleaning up the British Constitution you can't afford to wear gloves."

She had heard of Lord Sandgate, whose conduct in the Clark affair had made scandal; she observed him with interest. He was bowing to a great lady at the moment, stooping over her hand. She remarked upon his air of breeding. Oh, Rodono would allow that he was a gentleman.

"What else can a man be?" said she.

"Well, he can be a regicide," said Rodono.

"And is Lord Sandgate a regicide?"

"Ah, I don't go so far as that. But I will affirm that if he could induce certain distinguished persons to *felo de se*, he would be satisfied with the day's work. He's perfectly sincere, mind you, and that is why he's dangerous. He truly believes that Castlereagh is a villain—which is nonsense; and is sure that the Wellesleys have England by the throat. He strangles in his own stock when he remembers it."

He returned to her own affairs, and the more readily because he found a new note in her which charmed him, a note of timidity, of maiden bashfulness, of softness. Beautiful as he had always found her, he had sometimes thought her over bold. There was nothing of the sort in her now.

"Don't upset yourself," he told her. "I'll do what I can. He must be got out, of course—and he shall be. But I'll muzzle old Cobbett and send Bob Ranald off to sea. I'll do everything—anything—for you." He felt very tender, and stopped himself there; but when she gave him her hand he held it for a moment.

"You are very kind to me," she said when she had recovered her hand. "I am grateful, indeed. I feel so much alone here. My people—even my brother—see things differently. I have no one to talk with of what papa and I were always full—I mean right things, noble things—justice and—equality. Oh!" she cried out, and her eyes filled; "this is a horrible place."

It was comical, he felt, though he was a good deal touched by it. A fellow the more in gaol—and a lovely girl in tears for him! What the devil was it all about? I think it shows how puzzled he was that he began to want to dispose of her somehow. He advised her to go down to Petersham, to his sister Grizel and her crocuses. She should go down and stay—Grizel would be proud. "Take yourself down there," he said, "and make yourself comfortable. It's a pretty place, and nobody in it but Grizel and the parent." The parent was the Earl of Drem.

Hermia thanked him. Yes, she would like that, if Lady Grizel would not mind and grandmamma would allow it. But grandmamma had ideas about young ladies' escorts. Did Lord Rodono think that Harriet Moon would do for chaperon? He thought she would do excellently. "I'll tell you what," he said, "I'll drive you down, if you'll come. Let's go and ask my lady."

Grandmamma was found to be in a good humour. Moon might go, certainly, she said, if Hermia wished it. She had no immediate use for Moon. But Lord Rodono's coachmanship was plainly declined.

So in due time Miss Hermia went down to Petersham,

to hide and, she hoped, to bury her troubles—in the Caryll chariot, with Moth in the rumble; and found Lady Grizel among her crocuses, a sandy-haired, gentle lady of certain years and fixed views upon marriage. Lord Drem was "somewhere about," spudding daisies on a lawn.

CHAPTER IX

PEACEFUL days, balmy of spring, of crocuses, budding lilacs, bursting thorn, live green vistas, succeeded; days of rest, refreshment, and the readjustment of balances warped by London. The young novice in affairs recovered her tone, and with that her virgin acerbity; before the end of this chapter she will be found —*contacta nullis ante cupidinibus*—hectoring Harriet Moon, much as her prototype, the Huntress of Arcady, rated the too-fond Callisto. Politics were unknown at Petersham, for Lord Drem thought of nothing but shorthorns and Border antiquities, and to Lady Grizel horticulture was almost a guilty passion. She was, for the rest, an amiable lady, incurably placid, who apparently set no bounds to her philanthropy. She had Harriet Moon knitting comforters for orphans before she had been in the house four and twenty hours, and bade her guests good-night at ten o'clock to go and sit up until daylight with one of the maids, who had a quinsy and was feverish. But her influence was no mere sedative; it was corrective and tonic. If she had no predilections for politics, she had no prejudices either. The monumental inertia of the Whigs did not make her angry, the gusty strivings of the reformers after a new heaven and a new earth only made her smile. Silly folk! when the *ribes* was in flower and the bees hung about it. She was some years older than her brother Rodono, and assured Hermia that she had known a great deal more of Lord Edward than he ever had. "I knew him well enough to love him," she said, "and to see that he was a perfect little goose. He had his flowers at Frascati, and his Pamela, and his devoted, dear, foolish mamma—what more could the man want?" For all that, she was pleased to know that Rodono had joined the Reformers. Hermia had not known it, but such was the fact. There had been a dinner at Sir Francis's, in Piccadilly, and a meeting at the Crown and Anchor, where Rodono, introduced by Mr. Ranald, had spoken—quite well. "It seems that this is your doing, my dear," she continued, "and honestly I'm much obliged to you. It will give the dear fellow something to do and keep him out of mischief. Since he left the army he's thought of little but horses. I've been uneasy about him."

Miss Chambre had been confused at this revelation of her influence, but Lady Grizel seemed to have no doubts. "Tom thinks very highly of you, Hermia, and I cannot see why you should not be told. It is a great thing to make him serious, and no real harm can come to him. He's not like Mr. Ranald at all—not the kind whom they send to the Tower. He's very amusing, but that is because everything amuses him—even politics. I'm sure it's a very good thing, since he has to be in Parliament. It wouldn't amuse me at all—at least, it hasn't hitherto. But if Rodono is to be a Reformer, I suppose I must see what I can do."

Old Lord Drem took much off his daughter's tolerant view. When he had been Rodono's age, he admitted, he had been involved in politics, but now he knew better. "I do not often find myself in agreement with Monsieur Voltaire," he told Hermia, "but I must say that if everybody was as good a gardener as Grizel there would be no politics, because there would be no time for them. I am told that your bright eyes, my dear, have turned my son to digging other people's ground. It is to be hoped that he'll dig more vigorously there than he has done in his own seed-plot. Curiosity will help him, possibly. No, no, I make no complaints of your brother, Grizel—don't think it. But I fail to see how a young man can remove motes if he has shown no disposition to engage with beams—the Scriptures are with me, I believe—and I doubt whether much will come of it. A Reformer, you tell me? Well, well, we are all of us that, I hope."

This was all very wholesome and tonic. It reduced murdered horses to normal proportions, and bare-headed young heroes too. When Lord Rodono paid the ladies a visit, he found that he could make himself welcome without fresh details of tyranny; and as he had nothing to report, he was glad to be spared the pains of inven-

tion. He rowed them on the river and talked nonsense—
a much better plan.

But another visitor—shot suddenly out of the blue, in a
dog-cart of a bright red colour, with two skittish chestnuts driven tandem—caused a great commotion among
the Petersham crocuses. This was Lord Morfa's appari-
tion, not to be accounted for by avuncular interest in Miss
Chambre, nor by esteem for Lady Grizel's virtues. However, he came, he descended from his cart wonderfully arrayed, was exceedingly affable to the ladies, and full of
explanations. He had brought, he said, letters for Hermy
and various messages from her grandmother; he hoped
that Lady Grizel would forgive the scant ceremony
which he had shown her. But town was monstrously
dull, upon his word of honour, and he owned that he had
jumped at the chance of doing Hermy a service, prin-
cipally because it would serve his own purpose exactly.
The country was his passion, it would seem; he was never
so happy as when he was at Wrensham or Morfa, or
some of his places. Flowers now! No one could help
liking flowers. Lady Grizel must give him some
wrinkles; she must, indeed—and he would take notes.
He dared not trust his memory.

He really did his best to be agreeable, and was so happy
that he became so. Hermia had never liked him so well;
he was turned into a frolicsome youth in place of the
withered, young-old dandy he showed to be in London.
He took the two girls out in the tandem-cart, ate curds

and whey at Richmond, patted the shorthorns, admired the crocuses, and listened for three-quarters of an hour to Lord Drem's account of his researches into the Raid of the Reidswire, which Ritson had so needlessly obscured. When, in the course of the afternoon, Miss Chambre retired to read her letters, she left him under this learned torment, bearing it like a little gentleman. (He called Lord Drem "sir," and she had thought that admirable.) But when she paused presently in her writing, and looked out of the window, there he was disappearing up the long grass walk with Harriet Moon. It was then that Hermia remembered the tell-tale brown eyes. What did this mean?

Lord Morfa stayed to dinner, sat after it with his host, drank tea with the ladies, heard Harriet sing and Lady Grizel play the harp, and did not take himself away until near ten o'clock. They heard his post-horn after that as far as Richmond Hill. Harriet sat in her friend's room, plainly listening for it—tense and bright by the open window—until Hermia drove her to bed in order that she might get into her own. But there, though she lay snug enough, she was by no means able to sleep. She had seen much in the course of that evening; Uncle Morfa's attentions were not to be mistaken; nor, if uneasy fingers, downcast eyes, and sidelong looks at the company were any evidence, was it possible to doubt that Harriet was flattered. Poor, foolish Harriet—but really, what was to be done? Oh, nothing, nothing! "I can't tilt at all Uncle Morfa's windmills," she groaned, restless in her bed. "The little wretch sets them up like mushrooms." Well, but was a poor brown-eyed Harriet, who had barely snatched her soul from the talons of a grandmamma, now to place it, a trembling gift, into the paws of an Uncle Morfa, of a crony of the Prince's? Very doubtful tales were whispered about this young man—she knew just that much and no more. She remembered now again his conduct—above all, his appearance—in the Vernour affair. Atrocious! Did it not stamp him finally?

And yet he had been charming that afternoon—for all the world like a boy home for the holidays. If that, after all, were the real Morfa? No—there had been a reason for that. He could stoop to please when he wanted something—all his kind could. He wanted Harriet, it appeared; did not that prove him a monster? Harriet—a little amanuensis—who cried in corridors and had experience behind her eyes. There was another Lord Morfa, wicked, tipsy, passionate. She grew hot all over as the initial scene of her entry into London came back to her. Too surely that was the real Morfa—that swearing, over-dressed lad, swung like a rag-doll by David Vernour—a man, he, if ever there was a man. Start that young man bare in the lists, and he would give an account of himself above all the Morfas, Crowlands, Rodonos of this world. Whereas—strip Uncle Morfa of his high-waisted coat and rolled collar, unwind his great stock, pull him down from his curricle, and what was there left but a little white-faced boy of unwholesome tastes? Such thoughts as these inflamed her and upset her crocus-rest.

In the morning Harriet, after much hesitation, and, as if driven by a kind of fate, opened upon Lord Morfa's visit. . . . "I heard the horn at midnight, Hermy," she said—her face not to be seen. She was leaning on the ledge of the window looking out towards Richmond.

"Then you must have listened for it, my dear," she was briskly told.

"Oh, Hermy! indeed——"

"Why should you be hurt? But I think you are a goose, for all that. Why should he blow horns at midnight? And he drives like the wind. It is the one thing he can do."

"Oh, Hermy, you are unfair. But—you think he drove directly to town? I could not help fancying. . . . Do you think he did?"

"I don't think about him at all. Why should I?"

"No, no—of course not. Why should you?"

"Harriet, do you?"

The girl turned a blenched face from the window where she sat.

"Oh, never, never, Hermy, I vow to you—oh, never, never, never! How could I dare to lift up my eyes? He is most kind to me—all that is kind. I think of him with gratitude and respect. To me—to such as I am—he must ever be noble—and splendid. Oh, what must you think of me!"

She was vehemently on the defensive—too vehemently. She looked fierce and tragic—fierce and tragic about Lord Morfa! And what on earth did she mean by her "noble and splendid"? Hermia's lip curved in scorn.

"Noble! Splendid! I don't think you can know what those words mean. Is it possible that you believe him noble and splendid?"

Harriet quailed. "You mean about—I know what you mean now. I don't understand how you take such an interest in— But, of course, in your position— May I say that you are severe?"

"I don't think that you may. Mr. Vernour has been in gaol for six weeks. And Lord Morfa disports himself here!"

Harriet could be bold on occasion, it seemed. She defended Lord Morfa. "It was because of the indignity; he could not suffer it. A scuffle—within his own gates!" And now Miss Chambre stared—her Dian look.

"You use very strange words, I think. Indignity! How can there be indignity done to what has no dignity?" Harriet was driven to her last trench; but she tried a shift or two.

"You press me hard—not very kindly. I can't answer you, and I ought not. Lord Morfa is your relative—you may say what you please of him; but he is the son of my benefactress, of my patroness—I will ask you to remember that."

Miss Chambre thawed at once. "You dear creature, I'm a wretch—and you're very loyal. That's what I try to be. We see things differently. Forgive me." Harriet was allowed to cry upon her bosom—but Hermia had no more to say to her of Lord Morfa, or of anybody else.

That afternoon marks a stage in her career. She went into the library after luncheon, searched for the book of her mind, found it, and never stirred until she had finished it. She read every word, from its sublime initial fallacy to the end of the first part—rhetoric or sophistry, what you choose to call it, it was necromancy to her; at every strophe of its exalted argument shapes rose, shapes sank, as their essential manhood was revealed beneath their rent vesture.

"Titles are but nicknames, and every nickname is a title. The thing is perfectly harmless in itself; but it marks a sort of foppery in the human character, which degrades it. . . . "

"The French constitution says, There shall be no titles; and of consequence, all that class of equivocal generation is done away; and the peer is exalted into Man. . . . "

"It is properly from the elevated mind of France that the folly of titles has fallen. It has outgrown the baby

cloaths of Count and Duke, and *breeched itself in manhood.*"

Breeched itself in manhood! O rare Tom Paine! She
arose from her perusal and paced the library in a state of
indescribable exaltation. She knew that she was trembling, and she knew why. The Rights of Man, to what
arm can carve, or brain wield, or heart command—she
owned to them all. The Rights of Woman, what were
they? To what heart can crave, and soul need, and body
supply. And all these rights could be reduced to two:
the Right of Man to take, and of Maid to give.

Lady Grizel came to find her out, to take her for a
walk. They were to go to Twickenham to visit in a
clergyman's family. The good man's lady had recently
presented him with a child—a fine little boy. Wholesome
descent from the heights for our young energumen.
Lady Grizel might always be trusted for that sort of
thing.

CHAPTER X

THE memory of Jane Countess of Morfa will undoubtedly endure in the minds of all those to whom the Regency day appeals, either as the end of the old or the beginning of the new English order, and substantial justice will be done to her if she is recorded as a stronghold of Privilege, one of the flanking towers of that Bastille, built in 1688, shaken in 1789, and condemned as unsafe in 1832. A tower she was, one of the last to yield to time and the age, and yielding, when she must, inch by inch. We shall have to see her at it. But as I desire to remind the reader that she was a human being, as well as an Institution, I must declare that she was by no means without some natural emotions. She loved her children and her children's children, and would have fought for them as keenly as any woman born. She had real benevolence, too, for other inhabitants of our globe —her cousin Sefton, her friend Lord Crowland, her county neighbour the Duke, and her brother, the Marquis of Badlesmere. If she stopped there, more or less—and she did—it was not because she had exhausted the world of objects of interest, but because you can't love people in masses unless you are a philanthropist or a clergyman. She was neither. The world, no doubt, did contain so many millions of souls, souls, indeed, resident in persons whom one met in society or heard of in the House of Lords; she had no reason to dispute that, and no concern. But these were hirelings, after all— and one does not precisely love one's housemaids. These millions were of the sort whom, in one way or another, one paid to do things for one. A Secretary of State? Well, one pays him. Sir Arthur Wellesley? He is for hire. A king, a king son's, an archbishop, a Chancellor? "My dear lord," she would say in her scissor-tones, "there is no difference in kind between the Prince of Wales and my mantua-maker. In degree there is much, and highly in favour of Madame Pelerine. She is not nearly so extravagant, and does her work cheerfully."

This being so, and I do but state it as I find it, it may be conceived how her philosophy had been disturbed of late, since she had been forced to recognise the existence of a person—a tradesman and a butcher—in grief for his son, and of such a man's son in gaol, awaiting his trial. The lion in the fowler's net is a good enough parallel. She ran through a swelling series of shocks; she had been surprised, amused, amazed, interested, incredulous, bored by turns. Then presently she grew angry, and at last all her phases of feeling, churning in her bile, drove in and in upon her nature, and she felt nothing but a deep-set resentment at the infamy which dared to threaten her. She was goaded into action. Disgusted at every step, she ordered the Caryll host; and her disgust, far from paralysing her efforts, gave them vehemency and persistence. Her way was made unexpectedly easy by the news that Vernour was of the Reform party; this had but to be known in the right quarter. She never, in so many words, gave Justice the nod; no direct message was ever sent to any one; she did her business much too well for that. It got to be understood that young Vernour was a seditious rogue, better in the King's Bench—and there young Vernour lay from January until the middle of March.

She was not vindictive—vengeance upon a tradesman, absurd!—but she was very angry, and sure that she did well. Mr. Aloysius Banks, of *The Edinburgh Review*, took leave to agree with her. Sharp examples were necessary if persons were to be taught their places in the scheme of polity, in these times above all when Clamour and Faction had combined against Order. If outcry was to be raised against kings, whom Families had established, how long, pray, before Families themselves were to be arraigned? That disgraceful affair of the Duke of York's, now! Of course, the man deserved what he got, but, of course, half the uproar had been aimed beyond him—to Windsor and to Brighton. That was to be understood, and she was not one to quarrel with it. No Radical on a tub could despise royalty more than that great lady. But she was forced to tell herself over and over again, as she beheld, not without some satis-

faction of her extreme contempt, the flounderings, snort-
ings, and bellowings of that harried Prince-Bishop of
York and Osnaburgh, that there but for the grace of
God floundered Roderick Earl of Morfa. There, grace
of God or none, must he never flounder! A trial of Vernour, evidence against Vernour, were unthinkable; an
Earl of Morfa in the witness-box! Forbid it, heaven!
Time after time, then, the young man was remanded, bail
refused; and as the Press was too busy to heed him
and the Duke of York large in the mob's eye, it really
seemed that Heaven had gone into partnership with an
old dragon of a countess fighting for her order behind
her spiked walls. She held on, and she won. March was
all but over, Lord Castlereagh was now the unmasked
villain of the hour, when Vernour the elder lost his nerve,
drooped his insolent head, made his prayer of humble ac-
cess at the tradesmen's gate one windy morning, and was
admitted into the presence of an offended patron.

She had expected him, waited for him, and now she had
him on his miserable knees. She was very capable of
playing out the scene with the majesty of a Siddons; but
she didn't play it at all. It was too real and too serious
for histrionics; she sat holding her crutch, nodding,
blinking her fierce eyes, working her lips—no longer
angry, but deeply incensed. Vernour the elder, by the
door, a fine, upright man, grey-haired and grey-whis-
kered, with a lined, dignified old face on him, bowed his
head as he humbled himself—a person in the presence

of Family. "My lady, I ask your pardon for my boy, I ask it on my knees. Indeed I do, my lady—in a bitter day for me. He forgot himself, my lady—my unfortunate son. He has a spirit—he is quick——"

A butcher with spirit! Quick! This was too much for Lady Morfa.

"Vernour, you are talking nonsense, and I cannot have it. It was not spirit, it was insolence. Such things are not to be borne. You see where they may lead—where they must lead."

He was very feeble now, admitting everything or anything.

"No, my lady, no, it is so. I know that he forgot himself—and dearly, dearly he's paid for it. Dearly—oh, dearly. Six weeks in gaol, with rips and street-walkers— my boy! My lady, he's my only son. . . . Why!"—he stared at his offended god—"why, my lady, 'tis enough to make a Radical of the lad. It is indeed."

"Man," said Lady Morfa, throwing back her head, "he *is* a Radical. Detestable."

Vernour shook his. "Ay, my lady, 'tis to be feared. I've known that to come of such a trial. I've known a young man go to gaol through no fault of his own, and come out after serving his time—and if he stop out thereafter 'twill be through no fault of his own. My lady, a man must speak up for his son—and such a son as he's been to me! A good lad, my lady, a clever, studious, spirited——"

Oh, unlucky word! "Vernour, I can't have it, and I
will not. Spirited! Do you know what was done? Do
you know that his lordship was—*touched? Touched* by
your son—touched on the collar?" That was as near
to the fact as she could get herself to go. "Do you know
that Lord Edlogan was also touched—touched upon the
—ah, *person?* Do you know what these things mean?
They mean Revolution, man; they mean the breakdown
of the Constitution. They must be dealt with—and they
have been dealt with. If persons act in this way, whole
classes of persons may act so; and society, and decency,
and proper order must cease to exist. You are a sensible
man, Vernour, and must surely perceive it."

"Yes, my lady, yes, indeed," says broken old Vernour.

"Very well. Then don't come to me talking of *spirit,*
because that tells me that you hope to justify what cannot and must not be justified."

"It has ruined my son, my lady; it has gone near to
ruin me. I've been in business now for forty years—
nothing but the best families, my lady—and can scarce
hold my head up again."

Her ladyship was not impressed. "I think you have
held it too high, Vernour, indeed I do. If you have been
taught to hold it more becomingly for the future, this
lesson will not have been without benefit. And your most
unhappy son—let him be encouraged by this to learn
how to keep his station in life. Latin! French! I never
heard such nonsense. How can you be surprised that

he's a Radical? Why, he might be—a pickpocket on these terms. But I have no wish to be harsh, now that you have come to your senses—none at all. I will speak to his lordship, use my influence with Lord Edlogan, with his Grace. I don't suppose that there is any desire to punish you for your son's offence; and I understand from you now that he is truly penitent, and not likely to indulge his wicked, most wicked feelings of disrespect again. Is that so?"

"Let me assure your ladyship———"

"Assure me by your actions, Vernour, and let your son assure me. That is all I have to say upon this distressing affair. No doubt the young man will now be set at liberty—and may resume his—ah, duties, here and elsewhere. I have no wish, I say, to be harsh. And I will speak with his lordship about the horse. Possibly, under the circumstances, he may be willing to consider what might be done."

"A blood horse—cost me thirty guineas—" old Vernour was understood to murmur. Up went Lady Morfa's head again, like the royal standard on a birthday.

"Thirty guineas! Oh, ridiculous! A person—that walk of life—a thirty guinea horse! Why, my grandson, Mr. Chambre, gave no more than sixty for his hackney. I am quite at a loss— Oh, ridiculous!"

"Very good, my lady," says poor Vernour. Lady Morfa was now sick of him.

"I will speak to his lordship—can make no promise, of course. That is all, I think, Vernour."

But he had to crawl a little nearer; business was business still. Her ladyship's patronage and custom—? Her ladyship reassured him; he could call as usual. She cut short his gratitude, waved him out, and went away to wash her hands. A very hateful, distressing affair.

And there, so far as she was concerned, the incident ended; yet just there, in a sense, it may be said to have begun. Family, or Franchise (according to Mr. Aloysius Banks), is a living thing, with a spirit as well as a body to it, which bloweth where it listeth. We have now to see it take a flight as high as strange. But Vernour the younger was brought up before the magistrate for the seventh time, and as no evidence was offered against him, and no remand applied for, he was set at liberty. A few mornings later his horse might have been seen tethered to the Caryll House railings, and himself, bareheaded, in blue frock and apron, at the tradesman's door, awaiting custom or riding his tray. And had his lordship passed out or in, not a doubt but that the young man would have touched his forelock—for, business being business, only insensate rage can obscure a lord from British eyes. Mr. Cobbett, it is true, did give a line or two to the thing in the ensuing *Register;* but the front page was occupied by Lord Castlereagh and the new Reding job. Mutterings, foamings from a man Hazlitt at Winterslow were nothing. No; there was an end of it, certainly, so far as Lady Morfa was concerned.

CHAPTER XI

MISS CHAMBRE came back to Caryll House early in April, in excellent spirits and blooming health. Petersham had done its work. Her cheeks were glowing, her bosom abud; her wit overflowed. Gentlemen at parties fell before her like butterflies to a high wind. My Lord Edlogan changed his course of life, and drank negus; Lord Rodono presented a petition to the House of Commons; Lord Sandgate sought an introduction; Mr. Banks wrote a poem, "To Miss H. C., on returning to Town." It was even rumoured that the Prince of Wales had asked two or three times if she was to be seen yet, and that Lady H— was greatly chagrined. She was taken everywhere, and everywhere admired, and seemed to have entirely recovered from her former fever.

But there was a good reason for that. The Rights of Man were drowned in the domestic affections. Dick Chambre, whom she adored, her handsome, gallant Dick, was to sail for Portugal at the end of a week, in the same ship that took Sir Arthur; his uniform, his servant, his baggage, his sword; the Bible which he vowed to read, the letter-paper which he swore to cover; the farewell dinners, the farewell pauses, in which only their hearts dared speak—here was enough to fill a sister's mind.

"Some natural tears they shed"—but not many, for Dick was mortally afraid of them, and she kept back hers for his sake, doing violence to her lips also, to her arms and fond heart. Had she hugged him, she would have cried; had she cried, God knows that he would have broken down. Their last night together was a piercing comedy of reserves, like many a night and day in England. She was desperately off-hand, he savagely matter-of-fact. It was "Good-night, Hermy. Shall I see you in the morning?" and "Yes, if I'm not too sleepy. Good-night." No kisses; and no tears until the door was shut—and then a stiff-chokered young subaltern on his knees at his bedside: "God bless her—God bless my Hermy—God bless me, Amen!" and a tumble-haired beauty with scalded cheeks, lying anyhow on a couch: "Oh, Dick! Oh, Dick! What shall I do?" That was the English way of it before the Reform Bill, and perhaps is so yet, unless the Radicals have got at human nature.

She saw him drive off in his postchaise, into the golden spring mist, without a murmur; and breakfasted sedately with grandmamma, as became a Caryll by the mother's side.

Some few nights later the Caryll in her showed its right to franchise, its indefeasible claim to prerogative of choice. You can't blame her—or I cannot. If she had the right to command herself, she had the right to let herself go. Logically, it's not to be denied that if you can set up you can also pull down, though custom be against it and its indulgence may well lead on to anarchy. However, here is what happened.

There was a dinner-party at Caryll House, which was to be followed by the usual assembly. Lady Morfa plumed herself upon these, or would have if she had been a common person, and held them weekly while Parliament was in session. The Whig families rallied, or else, so far as she was concerned, they ceased to be Whigs. In very flagrant cases they ceased to be Families. But the diners were always carefully chosen, and this one was a good specimen of its class; young men, for Hermia's sake—young men of worth and standing; a few of Morfa's friends, and a politician here and there, with possibly a wit—to give body. Lord Edlogan of the wounded nose was there, a very handsome stripling, not without brains, although he did his best to seem so; Mr. Horner also, whom Miss Hermia adored, and Lord Rodono, who adored Miss Hermia and did not care, now, who knew it; and Lord Sandgate was strangely there—but his family was undeniable, and the Clark affair had blown over. Lord Sandgate was presented on this occasion, and was to hand Miss Chambre in to dinner. Then there were Lady Diana Topham, whose husband would be a peer some day, and Mrs. Western, who went everywhere, though no one knew why; Lady Gorges, pretty, swan-necked, and a poetess; Sir George Coigne, the young Buckinghamshire baronet, a Botetort through his mother, therefore nephew of her ladyship, and enormously rich; lastly, Lady Barwise, eldest daughter of the house of Caryll, Princess Royal, you might say, of that strait realm—and Mervyn Touchett, the diarist, who was to give the dolorous stroke. Lord Morfa himself, it so happened, was dining at home, and allowing no one to be unaware of it. It is most certain that Miss Harriet Moon, suffusing and paling in the long drawing-room, where she was expected to be both before and after dinner, was aboundingly aware of it.

Lord Morfa led the talk, as was only natural. It was an age when conversation, to call it so, was apt to run in monologues. There seemed no middle course between that and general hubbub. But it cannot be allowed that the young man was fitted for his task; he mistook equivoque for epigram, and anecdote for information. He spoke of persons rather than of things, and his subjects were the more fortunate if they were not present. On this occasion, for instance, his fancy led him to discourse of M. de Montrond, a too famous gentleman of his own world, in a manner more facetious than respectful. He addressed himself, in true Caryll fashion, to his mother at the further end of the long table.

"Old French!" said he, chuckling—thus they designated M. de Montrond—"he's devilish clever. I know for a fact, ma'am, that he had ten thousand of Seph's money at White's. That's not so bad for a night's work, hey? And he fairly skinned Joliffe, I hear."

It was impossible to say whether Lady Morfa was edified. Lord Sefton was a kinsman—but there's nothing in that.

"Monsieur Montrond is very clever," she allowed, "very clever—with his hands."

Morfa guffawed over his wine, and allowed Lord Sandgate to take up the tale.

"He has a tongue, too—old Montrond. Did your ladyship hear what he said to Pink Mordaunt the other night? 'Pink, *mon vieux*,' says he, '*dépêchez-vous de reconnaître ce bon Monsieur Cobbett, ou bientôt il ne vous reconnaîtra pas*.' I call that uncommonly neat of Montrond."

Lady Morfa could see nothing in a story which had Cobbett for a personage, and stared rather blankly at her guest; but it was Cobbett's name which brought about a crisis. Mervyn Touchett was the instrument— a keen-faced man of thirty, with black hair, good grooming, a lisp, and an appearance studiedly unpicturesque. He had a fine pair of eyes, and knew it, but he had missed Lady Morfa's blank look. His teeth were excellent.

Leaning now sideways, to avoid a gold épergne, catch Sandgate's eye, and have a view of "the sumptuous Miss Chambre," as he was fond of calling her—"Your Cobbett, my dear lord," he said with mock severity, "your Cobbett strikes a note."

"He strikes more than that, Mervyn," said my lord.

"He hardly strikes the stars, though I grant you that he strikes at them. Pray, have you seen the *Register?*"

"I always see it," said my lord. "You find it stimulating?"

"Cayenne," says Touchett. "Morfa, you should look at it. You're in it—you're always in it now."

"Damn him, I know," Lord Morfa said; "but you may spare my blushes."

Lady Barwise peered up, scenting havoc. She hated her brother. "Pray, Mr. Touchett, spare Roddy nothing of that sort. He blushes so rarely, and is so become by the appearance *in every way* that I shall insist——"

"Thank you, Louisa. You always give a helping hand," said the little lord.

"I say, Touchett, is Edlogan in too?" This came from Sir George Coigne, baronet of Bucks, knight of that shire, and man of substance. The hunt was up at that end of the table, but had not yet reached her ladyship's. As for the unhappy Edlogan, he had trusted, blushing, to his luck; but it seemed that he, too, was in. "Yes, yes, Edlogan's in—nose and all that." And then it was that Miss Chambre lifted her head sharply and began to listen. Lord Rodono, with the eyes of a lover and the mind of one, remembered that look of hers; Diana's, on the uplands, sighting a quarry, eh? However that may be, she looked up as suddenly as a cat which hears a rustling in the grass, and, sleek before, is all at once sinewy and intent.

Mr. Touchett, so many eyes upon him, produced from his pocket-book a slip of paper, and threw it in silence to Lord Morfa—who stared at it, but did not take it.

"I don't want it, Mervyn. It's no sort of use to me," he said. "The thing's done and done with—but Louisa's longing to be at it." Then he picked it up and tossed it forward towards Lady Barwise.

Rodono gained it, and was about to make a spill of it, for the mercies of the candle. But she stopped that.

"Please, Lord Rodono, let us know the worst. Mamma, you will allow us?" Her shrill tones silenced the table all over. Lady Morfa, checked in her conversation with Mr. Horner, must know what this was all about. The whole thing had to be explained to her. Nobody in London could have done it but Lady Barwise.

The strain was severe, but the great lady could meet it. She knew this daughter of hers, and did no more than raise her brows. "Cobbett? Do you want to hear him crow? By all means." She resumed her conversation.

The scrap went back to its owner with Lady Barwise's, "Pray read, Mr. Touchett." The unhappy man looked for a direction from his hostess, which he did not get. A turn of a hair would have done—but no! Lady Morfa was talking about Cintra.

"Forge ahead, Mervyn," says Lord Morfa, and emptied his glass. He signed to Progers that it was empty. The only objection heard was Rodono's. "Why should Mervyn be allowed to be a bore?"

Lord Morfa said, "Tom, behave." Then Mr. Touchett had to read his piece.

"David Vernour," wrote Cobbett, "has been released from the gaol where the Caryll House gang thought fit to confine him—after six weeks. Mark the clemency of Mr. Fox's friends. I saw him no later than Tuesday. To his credit, though infinitely to their discredit, he will say little. *Every word he withholds is a smear upon the Whig Cabal.* As fine a young fellow as ever I saw in my life, an educated, high-spirited, clever, instructed young man, herded with street-walkers, purse-cutters, and shop-thieves for six weeks; refused a trial; ruined. No, by Heaven, he is not to be ruined! In spite of them all, I'll see to that. And why? Because a little atomy Earl of Morfa, K.G., Baron Rhôs, etc., was drunk, and staked a horse for Vernour. Because a Marquis of Edlogan, also drunk, tried a rescue and had his nose punched. Upon my conscience that is all. Now Vernour receives a FREE PARDON from my lady Countess of Morfa, and leaves the King's Bench with as many stains upon his character as she and her cub choose to put there. With my hand upon my heart I say, If this is the way of the Friends of 1688, of the Foxites, Crowland-Houseites, and Grenville-cum-Greyites, give me that of Pitt, Castle-reagh, Wellesley, and Co. Why, my Lord Melville's peculations were gallantry compared to these of her ladyship's. She 'forgives' David Vernour! But I need say no more at present. Indeed, I have said now more than Vernour will care about.   He's a gentleman—and there's a shrewder blow at them than I can hope to give."

Mr. Touchett, long before he was through with a task upon which he had so light-heartedly embarked, wished himself dead.   When it was over he knew that, with regard to Caryll House, dead he was.   Nobody but Lady Barwise had a word to say.

"Charming for you, Roddy!   Charming!"

Young Lord Morfa met her chilly eyes and laughed at them.   The rest took it in their several ways—Lord Edlogan with a deep blush, Lord Sandgate, after whistling below his breath, with a gaze steadily at the ceiling, Mr. Horner with extreme misery which nothing, he felt, but rapid exercise could abate.   Lord Rodono watched his Hermia; and as for her, in the full presence of that table and of her painted ancestors ranked behind and before it, she flooded with scarlet, and flashed upon her shameful kindred.   Lord knows what she might have done or said; it is certain that she was primed to do or say something. She was in the act to rise when Lord Sandgate took hold of her gown and held her bodily in her place.   As she turned upon him in her fury—startled into fury as one is, balked of some vivid purpose, he bade her sit down again.   "Keep still—it is madness," was what he said, and saved her.   Lady Morfa had seen nothing so far. The girl sank back into her place, and lifted her head no more.

All this had taken but a half-minute, for all had happened in the first shock. It was as near an approach to a scene as her ladyship could ever have permitted, and such as it was she stopped it by a recovery little short of sublime. But she hurt Mervyn Touchett.

"Gusto spoils your reading, I consider. You roll it on the tongue." Her voice had a croaking sound—rather like the dry rattle of a corncrake. Her only other comment was apart to Mr. Horner, that for a barnyard cock it was stoutly crowed. No doubt, to that kind of fowl, the dome of St. Paul's, should he find himself upon it, would seem but a larger dunghill.

Mr. Touchett never entered the Caryll House gates again.

CHAPTER XII

A SPRINKLING of untimely guests were already in the great drawing-room when the ladies' procession entered it—new-comers, people of little account, persons. They seemed to huddle like sheep as the dining party rustled in; it was almost certain that Mr. Aloysius Banks stamped his forefoot when he heard her ladyship's crutch. Hermia, at least, told Harriet that she had heard him. She was now very calm, and able to be amused with her fellow-creatures.

Harriet commented upon the length of dinner. The servants had left the dining-room half an hour ago, and her ladyship rarely stayed ten minutes after that. "Mr. Touchett was reading to us," she was told.

"Really! A poem?"

"Yes," said Miss Chambre, "one might say so. It moved me a good deal. And now I want to run away and think about it. And so I shall if grandmamma doesn't catch me."

"Oh, Hermy," said her friend, whose ideas ran in a groove, "Lord Rodono will be so disappointed."

"I thought he was consoling himself when we left," Miss Chambre said.

"I could see that he was very much put out that you were given to Lord Sandgate."

"That was selfish of him—for I was very much honoured."

"You were happy with——?"

"With Lord Sandgate? Perfectly. He was very kind to me. Adieu, child." She kissed her hand to Harriet and flitted out on the tips of her toes. Tom Rodono, entering with the rest of the men in due time, found the rooms full—but emptied of her. Miss Moon took leave to tell him that Hermia had had a dreadful headache. "Don't wonder at it," said he; and then she had the story out of him.

Miss Chambre, who never suffered from headache, had an excellent night's rest, having sought it without any fuss of dedication to a cause or a duty. And yet, before she closed her eyes, she had made up her mind as to what must be done. Her prayers were as usual, without a long breath of preparation; if you had likened her to Antigone she would have been amused. She rose at her usual time, but did not ride as usual, and in the course of the early morning told Harriet Moon that she had some shopping to do, and would like a companion for the walk.

Harriet showed her evident pleasure, interspersed with the customary apprehensions. Would her ladyship—? Might not her ladyship—? That kind of half question was frequent upon Harriet's pale lips. A footman, too,

seemed almost a necessity; but Hermia said, Rubbish.
She intended to go and be back early; and—this was to
another aposiopesis—No, she had not thought of asking
grandmamma, unless Harriet might fall into disgrace.
A look into the brown eyes, which had begun to loom,
decided that. Very well, then, let grandmamma be asked.

Leave was obtained, but they must be back by noon.
Bond Street was the place? Very well; but in that case,
be back by half after eleven. At ten, the pair set out.

In that day of dangerous elegance, when women's
clothes surely fitted as closely to their minds as to their
pretty persons, Miss Chambre, by no means unaware of
her natural advantages, affected a simplicity and a daring disastrous to mankind. It would be as pleasant to
give a picture of herself as of her London, into whose
sunny spaces of grass and fleecy skies, among whose old
ruddy houses she walked that morning of the fifteenth of
April; for hers was a day when London was still a clean
country town and beautiful young women were not afraid
to show themselves in it. You may see them in print
and picture, in their feathers and fal-lals, their high-
waisted, low-bosomed gowns, airing with artful grace
their white stockings and their sandals, their Leghorn
bonnets and fluttering scarves; and in some such garb of
white and clinging silk you may clothe her, and in some
such close bonnet set her ardent face. Heightened as her
colour was by some resolve she had, her beauty showed
that rich and serious cast which must needs draw all male

eyes and yet remain unaffected. She was very ignorant
of such a battery. And she had lived most of her life,
too, in a country where women still knew how to walk;
she moved easily and well, did not mince her steps. She
moved and held herself, in fact, as a girl does who walks
to get from one place to another, which is not the present
fashion.

They crossed the Green Park and struck into Piccadilly without much talk. Miss Chambre was noticeably
quiet, and parried Harriet's utmost ingenuity. Anything direct she answered with "Yes," and "No." She
did not know yet what she was going to buy; no, she was
not going to Madame Pelerine's; she was not going to
the bonnet-shop. That was Lord Drillstone who bowed?
She had not recognised him. Mr. Touchett's poem of
last night? She had not said it was a poem. She had
said that it had moved her. Oh, had Hermy heard that
Mr. Cobbett—by accident? And then for a moment she
had paralysed Harriet with a look. "How do you hear
things by accident, Harriet?" Miss Moon, finally, with
a little sigh, resigned herself to her friend's larger mind
and more settled purpose. The Harriets of the world
win only by waiting.

They went north-east by devious and mostly unfre-
quented ways to the corner of Brook Street, unnoticed
and untroubled; there Hermia stopped. Harriet noticed
at once that her colour was high and her breath quick.

"Harriet," she said, "I have an errand in a shop near

here. Go into the bun-shop and wait for me. I'll not be
five minutes." The bun-shop was beside them. Through
its little panes of bottle-glass you could see the buns
arrayed in sticky pyramids, the glasses of sweetstuff,
brandy-balls, and bulls-eyes, and cases of jumbles, crisp,
curled, and fresh. The girl in charge, ringletted and
high-combed, peered through the window to see the fine
lady and her companion.

Harriet, on the verge of a secret, was uneasy.

"Dearest, what are you going to do? I fear some im-
prudence! What shall I tell her ladyship?"

"You will tell her nothing. I shall have that to do. I
am going to her directly I return."

"Is it—? Ought I not—? Oh, Hermy, I beseech you
to be careful!"

"I have been caring all night and all this morning,"
said Miss Chambre. "I hope there's been carefulness
enough." Human nature could not bear such things.
Harriet thrilled.

"Where is your errand? I vow that I have guessed it.
May I not—? I do think that you should tell me. Not
that I am in the least curious; I beg you to believe it.
But——"

Hermia was looking along Brook Street, and spoke as
one in a dream. "I think I cannot tell you—now, or at
any time. But no doubt you will hear."

"Oh, Hermy! Oh, darling!"

Hermia now looked at her; she smiled kindly, but shook

her head. "I think that I must not. It will be better for you—and for me, too—if you don't know it. I am doing what is right. I can assure you of that."

Harriet bit her lip. "I shall be most unhappy. You don't trust me."

"No, perhaps not. But it is impossible to me to talk. I have made up my mind. Please go and eat your buns. I'll have one afterwards." Harriet shivered, but obeyed.

Miss Chambre walked on alone, eastward, to near the Bond Street corner; near enough to it to be able to see the faces of the lounging dandies passing up and down —and to be seen. Hunchbacked Lord Sefton, in his bottle-green coat, saw her and saluted with great formality. Mr. Byng, who was with him, marked the attention, turned, saw her, and off with his hat. She bowed her head slightly and held back until they were gone on. Little things like these, to her who had never yet walked a London street without escort, made of her venture a journey of knight-errantry. Her heart was in her mouth, and, worse than that, her fears came thronging to her brain. She had been prepared for shame and terror—afterwards, but had counted on doing her errand with a rush. To think it out, to foresee the stages of it were madness; she simply could not afford it. And to be delayed, checked in the career—to be spoken with, held in talk, put back to the lists, to run anew—ah, no! Before she could be endangered again, taking now a full breath, she stepped through the little wicket of a shop-doorway, and stood in the sawdust, and inhaled the faint odours of the establishment of Vernour and Son, family butchers.

A pale young man stepped out of a sort of glazed cage and bowed before her. He was in frock and apron, and his hair was as smooth as butter—black butter. Also, he was dreadfully obsequious.

"At your service, madam."

Below her heart-beats and the sea-sound in her ears she heard her own strangled voice. "Is Mr. Vernour within? Young Mr. Vernour?"

The young man's raised eyebrows were intended to show deference, not surprise—but they were disconcerting, because they delayed her. "Mr. David, madam? I think not, but I will enquire. Permit me, madam."

He brought forward a chair, on which it was impossible to sit, though her knees were faltering under her. To sit down—here—when at any moment she might have to fly—to hide herself—never, never. In the meantime, the young man had disappeared, and she was alone with her heart-beats and a white-faced clock whose pulsing hammered at her brain.

He seemed gone half-an-hour, and every throb of the time added to her distress. She had never known before how conspicuous she was, how terribly under enquiry. A street-singer was quavering his endless ballad outside in the street, watching her with an eye which seemed to read her very soul, though no doubt it yearned for

nothing more than halfpence. A cart rattled by; the
boy in the tilt stopped whistling when he spied her. A
young gentleman drove past in a cabriolet, and the
groom dancing behind caught sight of her white dress,
and stooped to see her face. And then a closed carriage
with two fine horses pulled up short—oh, heaven, she was
in a trap! No—thank God, she need not hide herself—
it had gone on. She had determined that nothing should
compel her to that shame, but by now her blood was as
water.

When she heard steps within the glass door at the back,
the stricken beauty faced her assize. The door yielded
the tall figure of a man, but an elderly man. Old Mr.
Vernour, grave and grey, was bowing, and rubbing
propitiatory hands. He was ridiculously the humble
servant of any one with a shilling to spend; and yet she
eyed him as if he was new-risen from the dead.

"Your servant, madam, your servant. Your ladyship
was enquiring for—my son?"

"Yes, if you please."

It hurt Mr. Vernour to deny a lady; he spoke very seriously. "I grieve that he is absent, on his daily business.
It is most unfortunate." He looked sideways at her,
stroking his chin. "Can I—any message? I should be
truly honoured."

It was so impossible as to be almost absurd. She became
voluble in excuse. "Oh, no, thank you, Mr. Vernour—
indeed, no. I could not dream of troubling you. It is

of little or no consequence—indeed, it is really nothing
—to your son."

But Mr. Vernour still stroked his chin, not finding himself at all able to believe that such visits could be nothing
to his son. "Should I, madam—could I—mention a
name to my son?"

A name! The thought of it! "Oh, no, indeed, I won't
trouble you—so small a thing! My name is, of course,
nothing to your son. He does not know it, has never
heard it."

"Oh, madam!" Mr. Vernour was shocked at the
thought. A lady—a fragrant, floating, white-robed
lady of fashion, and his son ignorant! And he, good
man, ignorant himself, as the babe new-born!

Then, while he could hardly venture to look at her, so
discomfited was he, it came upon her with certainty that
she must fly. She had done her honest best, and had
failed. Her heart sank at the thought that all must
be done again. On some day still to come she must face
Bond Street again, again pass the wicket, stand, ask,
wait, be served by deferential old men—and could she
do it? She had no notion, but the question did not
press. What was urgent was that she should go, and
most urgent of all, the ridiculous puzzle of how to go.
Should she give her hand to old Mr. Vernour? Would
he take it if she did? Or should she bow, smile upon
him, thank him? All her self-possession was gone, all
her decision; even her imperative reasons for coming

on this errand at all were washing away on the ebb. Beauty in distress, helpless, miserable, shamefaced, and absurd—there really seemed nothing for it but that refuge of heroines, a tear-storm. And then, as she swayed and turned half, her affair was upon her. There came the canter of a horse, a sudden scour on the cobbles; and before she could collect her thoughts a tall young man stood bareheaded in the doorway, a tall young man with high colour and very light hair, and that look of resolute ability upon him which she had once before seen and never forgotten; and, frocked and aproned as he was, with his wooden tray under his hand, there was no majesty in England at that hour before which she could have stood so humbly. And yet the relief which his presence gave to her irresolution and discomfort was one of the strongest things about him. He was a tower of refuge; she would fear no more.

He bowed, and would have passed her, but "David, this lady—" began Vernour, the elder, and waved her into debate with a respectful hand.

"You wish to see me, madam?" She raised her eyes to meet his and faltered no more; for now the hour was come.

She spoke slowly and deliberately. "Mr. Vernour, I belong to a family which has disgraced itself in your eyes and in mine. I am come here to admit it fully, so far as I can, and to beg your pardon. I wish that my grandmother could have come herself, but she is an old lady, and you must excuse her. And I ought to say that she does not know that I have ventured to see you." The young man made as if he would come to her, but she stopped him. "Of course, I shall tell her immediately what I have done. I should not wish you to suppose that I would deceive her in such a matter. And I must say that I cannot expect your forgiveness for—for an intolerable act, but that I cannot gain my own without asking you for it. I hope you will be generous."

And there she stopped, because she had learned no more. She had trusted to her ardour to give her continuance— which it did not, but played her false. That quick movement of his towards her had thrown her out. She had thought he was indignant at a thing done by her in secret, and had made haste to disavow any secrecy. And then it had not been easy to go on; and now it seemed ridiculous to stop. At this point, too, her eyes fell before Vernour's, though his held their gaze. He had narrowed them, they had intensity; she felt them dreadfully upon her, and drooped under the steady attack. It was a full minute before he spoke.

"Madam," he then said, "is it possible that you are from——?"

Her lips faltered the admission, but immediately afterwards, as if ashamed of her weak knees, she held up her head and announced herself distinctly. "I am Miss Chambre. Lady Morfa is my grandmother."

Once again he deliberated his full time before he said,

"I think the Queen of England cannot be a prouder lady than you." He was very still, very trenchant; she thought him angry with her.

"You think that I have come to insult you. You have every right to think so; but it is not true."

If he had thought so, he must have been mad, but there was fire behind his voice when he answered her. And he held his hand up lest she should say any more.

He said, "I think that you are very proud; and you have made me proud. No greater honour was ever paid to a man. I have done nothing to deserve it—but I shall never forget it."

It was plain, even to her in her distress, that he was moved. His voice was husky, and his eyes were dim. But he did not for a moment cease to regard her; without any glimmer of offence he showed that he was absorbed in her. Not her beauty alone could have drawn such an intent scrutiny; her rank alone would have prevented it. Whether it was the extraordinary nature of her errand, or the simplicity with which she had acquitted it, or her dignity in difficulties, or her appeal—something there was which took him out of himself and made him strong while it made her weak.

Turning at last, but reluctantly, as though he was afraid she might vanish, he spoke to his father. "Father, how am I to prove to this lady what she has done for me?"

To old Mr. Vernour the incident had been dreadful. It

had upset all his theories; he was not able to do more than shake his head. "I doubt you cannot—I doubt you cannot." He could not lift himself; he seemed to be thoroughly ashamed. "I doubt this is too great an honour for you, my son. I doubt 'twill exalt you too greatly—for your peace of mind." He looked profoundly unhappy, spoke towards the sawdust of the floor.

This humility distressed her, and it appears that the young man must have divined it. The diversion which he proposed was well conceived; it seemed to give her the power of conferring another favour. She remembered it afterwards, and saw how high-bred it had been. He had asked her whether she would consent to make the acquaintance of his mother. "You will add to the obligation which we feel so truly," said he. "You will give a proud son a proud mother." She was very grateful, would gladly go in.

As he held open the glass door for her, she seemed to pass in beneath his arm. This was the effect, at least, which his height had upon her, and her consciousness of his eyes' downward fire, beating, as it were, like rays of light upon the lids of her own. She felt like a bird under the hand, fluttering her wings.

She was ushered into a dusky oval parlour, lit from a skylight. It was extremely neat, stiff, and unoccupied; it was like a miniature. He begged her to wait there while he found his mother. He pushed further into the interior, and she heard his plain voice call "Mother—where are you?" She did not sit, though she was desperately tired. You don't sit in kings' houses.

Mrs. Vernour came in, the softer, more blurred copy of her son—tall, largely made, fair and high-coloured, very self-possessed. For her, it was clear, the lovely Miss Chambre and her wild errand had no glamour. She must have been a splendid young woman herself, in her day; and it was at once apparent that she was a Scot. "Your servant, Miss Chambre," she said sedately. "My son David has told me of the honour done to him. Indeed, he would have gone through more for such a reward at the end of it." To Hermia's renewed protestations she deferred. She was perfectly the lady of breeding; she waived all injuries and griefs—and yet did not make too little of them, lest she should seem thereby to minimise the act of grace. Her ladyship, she suggested, had been taken aback. It was for her own son she had taken up arms. She hoped that, as a mother, she could understand a mother's feeling. The affair had ended— and this visit was the happy end. There was no more to be said. . . .

She fell to discussing her son. He had not been ill-treated; they had allowed him his books. He was a great scholar; a good son and a great scholar.

Hermia had heard that, she said, from Mr. Ranald—a friend.

"And a good friend to my son, Miss Chambre. The
Honourable Mr. Ranald. My mother was housekeeper
to his own lady mother at Drumlaw. 'Twas Lady Clanranald gave me my wedding-gown. And Mr. Robert was
born that same year in which I was married." Details
followed, from which it was made clear that David was
fourth child but the only surviving.

David was a scholar. He had been to the Bluecoat
School—had his Latin and Greek. Holy orders had been
his desire, but the death of his brother had decided him
against it; he had stayed by his father and never complained. But he had his interests—his life was very
full. His books, his debating. He was a keen politician, staunch for Mr. Cobbett and Reform. He was a
Westminster freeholder himself—had his vote. He had
taught himself the French, he would travel some day.
Meantime, he did his duty and was all that a son should
be.

She owned to his quick temper; that horse had been the
apple of his eye. It was on that horse that he used to
ride every Sunday to Feltham, where he had a friend—
a nursery gardener. David had many interests, it
seemed.

Cake and wine had been produced while this was going
on; Miss Chambre, now happy and at ease, forgot the
time, and did not disguise the interest she felt in these
confidences. She tried to express herself as she rose to
go. "I should like to tell you, Mrs. Vernour, how proud

I am that you should talk to me like this. I feel—that
I ought to be ashamed—to be———"

"It will be a sore day for England when the likes of you
are made ashamed, Miss Chambre."

She then took leave, hoping that she might come again.
Vernour was at the glass door as she came out. She
was very shy.

"Your mother has been extremely kind," she told him.
He bent vehemently towards her, then controlled himself.
"But you have been more than kind. You cannot know."

"No, no—not that." Her eyes appealed.

"If to give manhood back to a man be not a royal
act———"

She spoke her cry from the heart.

"Don't say those things, please. You rob me of what I
hold dear. I hold our honour very dear."

"You do, indeed," said Vernour. "It is certain that
you do." Her eyes filled at his praise. "Madam," he
continued, "I speak the truth. You have given me manhood back. I was like to have lost it on a time, and now
I know that I need not. Madam, madam! I could go
down on my knees to you."

"I beg you, I beg you—" This must be ended somehow. "You have been very kind to listen to me—and to
make light of what you endured. You have made me
happy. I know that you will forgive us. I see that you
are generous. You will excuse me if I—" She held
out her hand, and Vernour, fiercely red, took, bent over,

and kissed it. No more was said. She escaped like a bird out of a window. She ate no buns.

Homeward, then, like a bird on the wing, she sped, Harriet trailing in her wake—not to be talked to. "Don't talk to me, please—I cannot talk now. Yes, yes, I have everything I wanted. No—there are no parcels for you to carry."

Dandies ogled in vain; no doffed hats touched her, no beckoning hands from great carriages beguiled her from her thoughts. Arrived at the house, she went directly into her grandmother's room and spoke her piece. She found her at her letters.

"Grandmamma," she said, "I have come to tell you where I have been. I left Harriet in the bun-shop, and went on alone to Mr. Vernour's. I saw his son, and begged his pardon for the way we had used him. I conceived that his due."

CHAPTER XIII

IN WHICH WE RAISE OUR EYEBROWS

IT was much more than tradition with Lady Morfa that under no circumstances must there be a scene; it was religion—an act of faith; it was the only possible unfaltering tribute to her position in the scheme of the Universe, due as much to herself as to the Power that had placed her there. But there is more in it than the instinct which says, I am of the Rock; there was the other, reminding her perpetually, You are not. She was fatalist as well as stoic.

On the occasion just recorded there was undoubtedly a perceptible pause—a time of heart-panic for the girl, and for the lady a time during which she sat looking into vacancy, motionless except for the blinking of her white eyelashes, and for a trembling so slight that it could scarcely have been discerned by anybody, and certainly not by her grandchild. She recovered herself almost at once. Her tongue went twice to her lips, her hand twitched a little; and then she said, with extreme politeness—

"Will you have the goodness to repeat yourself, and more slowly?" Even this concession to the frailty of her age she would have forborne had she been able.

Commanding her nerves, the girl obeyed her, and had the good sense not to add a word to the bare announcement. Again Lady Morfa was silent for a while; and during that pause it is safe to affirm that if by any conceivable act she could have humiliated this child, she would have stooped to use it. There was one—there was one thing she could have said, plainly or by innuendo, which might have brought her to her knees; but it shows how fallible the youngest of us may be, in our interpretation of our neighbours, that Miss Harriet Moon's reading of her in just such a crisis as this was entirely at fault. It never entered Lady Morfa's head that Vernour was a fine young man or that her granddaughter was a fine young woman. What she saw with blank dismay was a chit of a girl who had upset her authority, and done it in so simple a manner that she was powerless to reassert it without becoming absurd. Once before she had been defied, by this child's mother; but Lady Hermione had climbed her wall in the night, had fled the country with Dick of the Gallop—while this Hermia Mary acting, in the broad light of day and Bond Street, had walked out of the gates, and returned to take her punishment. Now, the serious thing was that there was no punishment to give her. Anti-climax was unavoidable, since the death penalty was out of date. The baffled lady, driven to temporise, maintained her dignity unruffled. It was all she had left her at the moment.

"I think that I understand you," she said; "that is, I hear what you tell me you have done. Further than that I cannot go. You may have reasons for compromising yourself which—" The girl's lip trembled, but she burst in upon the icy stream——

"Oh, grandmamma, how could you have been so cruel? How could I bear it!"

"No discussions, please, Hermia." She put up her hand. "Those are out of the question between you and me. You will go to your room, if you please, and remain there until I send for you."

Miss Hermia had risen to hear her sentence. "I will do as you wish," she said, and turned, and reached the door. There she stopped for a moment, and came swiftly back.

"I must tell you this—" she spoke with passion. "You will do a great injustice to Harriet if you suppose that she knows anything of what I have done. Nobody knows of it but you."

"You forget Vernour and his family, I think," said Lady Morfa, and sent the blood to her cheeks.

"Naturally I don't forget the person to whom I had to go. But neither he, nor Harriet, nor any one in the world knew that I intended what I have done; nor did I know it until last night. So that Harriet——"

Lady Morfa nodded sharply. "I believe you. I cannot suppose that you would have told anybody whom you believed to be sane that you intended what you tell me you have done. And since you seem to be in doubt, I don't mind assuring you that I am not in the habit of speaking to Moon about your affairs or my own."

Hermia still stood, hovering, as it were, on the edge of tears. A look or a gesture would have brought her down, her face in the old woman's lap. Her story would have been sobbed out, her wondrous good reasons, and her wondrous bad ones. And it is very possible—I speak with reverence—that Lady Morfa's eyes were dangerously charged; that Lady Morfa, had she dared, would have opened her arms. But she could not for the life of her. Hers was that nature which must wear a mask or feel naked. To have tears is as shameful as to be drunk; in each case you exhibit yourself as you are, instead of as you intend to be—and that's the unforgivable act. It is a mistake to think that either she or her grandchild was unemotional; each went vibrating with emotion. The only difference in the pride they both owned to was that where the elder would never admit to feeling what was asked of her, the younger would never deny it. So there stood one with her heart in her hands, and there sat the other with hers in a cage—and the tale goes on.

In a few seconds more Miss Chambre was out of the door and upstairs; and all that Harriet could learn was that she was in her own rooms and would remain there for the present.

The daily and nightly round of Caryll House was not to be disturbed by the incredible acts of a little Miss

Chambre; but, nevertheless, Lady Morfa was more per-
turbed than she could have ever been brought to confess.
Metaphorically she may be said to have lifted up her
hands at a thing which passed belief. And she saw it,
mind you, at its full value; it was no mere silly gush of a
school-girl. Had it been so, a day or two's bread and
water would have requited it. No, but it had a symboli-
cal force; it was a surrender of the whole Whig position
to a beleaguering horde, whose mass and momentum she
felt as keenly as anybody. It was an act of treachery
from within quite beyond experience. The man Vernour
was a Radical, known to be a Radical, supported by the
whole reforming press. She had taken her stand against
him from the outset; she had strained the law—she knew
that; she had not disdained the assistance of the official
enemy to combat this new invasion, which she could see
was far more serious to her order than a whole country-
side of Tories. And she had won—she had stooped and
won. And now she was betrayed into the hands of her
foes in such a way that she could not even cry out against
the traitor. She could do nothing; she was perfectly
powerless. If she treated Hermia as she deserved, she
would exhibit the magnitude of her own defeat; if she
overlooked the affair, she would seem to admit the knowledge of her own deserts. Never was an ancient and great
lady in such a quandary.

Next, a sudden blow—from an unexpected quarter indeed—was like to have quelled her. When she told her

son, as she thought it her duty, what had been done against the house of Caryll, the young lord replied with the astounding words, "She's a good plucked one, I must say." He went on to add that she had done what he ought to have done long ago—that, by God! he was very much obliged to her, and should tell her so. That he did not was simply due to his mother's positive entreaty. She did not attempt to argue with him upon the merits; in fact, he had robbed her of the power to do that; but she said that if that were done, she should leave London and never return to it—and he gave way. But he frankly told her that he knew he had behaved "damn badly," and that if the fellow had not raised his dander he should have apologised. "Upon my soul, ma'am, it was his due. If I'm a gentleman, as I suppose I am, that's the line of country to follow. But I got cross, and then you got cross—and there's no going back then. By my soul and body, though!" and here he whistled, his hands deep in his breeches pockets— "by my soul and body, but that gel's a game chicken!" He rose to go. "She's done our work for us, ma'am, and I for one am very much obliged to her. I'm going to Brighton this afternoon—sent for this morning—says he must have me; so I'll bid you good-bye, ma'am. But when I come back I do hope I shall find Miss Hermy on your lap again—I must say that."

This, too, was more or less the opinion of Lord John Botetort, Lady Morfa's own and favourite brother, to

whom in her perplexity she confided the tale. He was a
tall, lean-headed gentleman, something of a buck and a
viveur, a club-man and great patron of the opera. His
white whiskers were close-cut and carefully brushed forward, his buckskins were flawless and apparently seam-
less, his coat was of bottle-green. "Jane," he said, and
confirmed it with an oath, "I'll tell you what it is. That
gal's too many for you—and a fine, free-spoken gal she
is. Jack Polperro had just such another—you remember
her, and what she did. The whole country knew it—half
of 'em saw it, by George! And *he* was a farmer—gentle-
man-farmer, as they say; but Jack Polperro was never
the same man again. You marry her, Jane, or we shall
all be in the papers. By Gad, ma'am, we are in the papers already! It don't want much in these days to get
the mob about your windows or about your ears. Look
at the Prince—look at him, I say! Why, when he goes
down St. James's Street you'd think 'twas a thief-taker
going to be hanged. . . . This fellow of yours, mind
you, is a red-hot fellow—speaks in Old Palace Yard—
is in with Bob Ranald and Burdett—and all of 'em. I
tell you he's the pet of the public, and, mark my words,
if you don't look nine ways for Sunday, you'll get her
chaired beside him—sure as you're here."

Lady Morfa looked her bleakest. "I must send her
away, John—it's clear."

"If you send her away, my lady," said her brother, "you
send her straight to him—not a doubt of it. And if you

take my advice, you'll let the fellow alone. The less you handle him the better. You've handled him only too well as it is. Six weeks' chokee! Why, five guineas would have done it—at the start—and what's five hundred to getting in the papers? No, no—marry the gal out of hand—you'll have no trouble there, and let her husband have the training of her. I wish him joy."

And then, almost word for word, he echoed his nephew Morfa. "Not but what I admire her, you know. I do, uncommonly. There was pluck in that—the sort of pluck one is pleased to have in the family. Proper pride —what! a game-bird! Let me tell you, my lady, that if humble pie has got to be eaten, that's the way to eat it. Bolt it whole, by Gad! Zounds, sister, I'd marry the girl myself, take her off your hands, if I wasn't her uncle, and be proud of her. The girl who knelt to the butcher, eh? Fine thing in its way—you'll have Cruikshank at it before long, see if you don't. Damn fine thing, and if I could have done it, I would." He was anxious to see Hermia—couldn't do any harm, he supposed; but Lady Morfa was by no means of that opinion.

The daily and nightly round, however, went on undisturbed. Great persons came and went, diners, callers; great assemblies heard the Countess of Morfa announced from hall to stair, from stair-foot to stair-head, and thrilled, or were believed to thrill, as of old. The Earl went to Brighton, unconscious that he had disgraced his family; Lord Crowland did not, perhaps, observe that one pretty girl was absent from the long table, nor Mr. Rogers that there was a laugher the less. Mr. Aloysius Banks, dining at Caryll House for the first time in his vexed progress up the shining ranks of the Constitution, may have regretted that his "lovely friend" could not admire his triumph—but only for a moment. He admired it too sincerely himself to need any assistance. "Lady Morfa, in whose company I happened to be dining," or "dining at Caryll House the other day"—fine phrases. It is possible even that Mr. Banks may have learned something of her escapade—for the thing spread about town, as we shall see—and may have accorded himself a delicate mission with regard to it. There was a paragraph in the *Morning Chronicle* of a late April issue which seems plausibly his. "Those leaders of faction, whose attacks upon a noble house, by the very excess of their rancour, so singularly failed, have now renewed them in a more insidious form. Having failed to *destroy*, they now seek to *divide*. It has been freely said, in journals which it would be unbecoming to name, that," &c., &c. . . . "We are assured by those best entitled to judge that no member of the exalted house in question has taken leave of his senses, and need hardly add that, had he done so, Mr. Cobbett would be the last person to be apprised of it." Not unskilfully steered, by any means: he may be congratulated.

But are we, I wonder, to congratulate Miss Harriet Moon, when, not long after the incarceration of her friend, she goes up Brook Street on an errand of her own? That is what she did; and more: she went unerringly to the wicket-gate of Vernour and Son, and passed it. She braved the pale young man in the glass case, and asked to see Mr. David Vernour. Mr. David was in, and was not long in presenting himself either. She fancied that his face fell; her own was charmingly apologetic.

She begged pardon for interrupting Mr. Vernour, but imagined that Miss Chambre must have left her sunshade behind her when she called a few days ago. A white silk sunshade, ivory-handled, silk tassels. It was not to be found at Caryll House, and it was almost certain that she had had it in her hand. Miss Moon was positive—nearly positive—that she had seen it.

Mr. Vernour denied the sunshade. Not only was it not here, but Miss Chambre had not carried it. Had she asked for it?

No, Miss Moon could not say that. In fact, she had not been able to see Miss Chambre since that day. Miss Chambre had returned to Caryll House and had at once seen Lady Morfa—since which time she had been in her apartments. Miss Moon's brown eyes were very large at this minute, largely inquiring of the shop and the carcases of beasts which it contained—largely apprehensive and sympathetic; and they lighted presently upon Mr. Vernour's and were perceived to be dewy.

Vernour was observed by her to be very red, and to be

frowning.   She had reason to complain of his tone, which was short—almost surly.

"I trust that Miss Chambre is well?"

"Oh, indeed, I trust she is.   She is my dear friend.   And she was in the highest spirits on the day of our walk."

"I need not tell you, madam, that her welfare is much to us here."   He spoke with difficulty.

"No, indeed; that is very natural," said Miss Harriet. "She is—you will understand—liable to alternations of feeling.   Those who love her can allow for that; but some complain of it.   She is not easy to understand."   And then Miss Moon sighed.

CHAPTER XIV

IN divers ways and by sundry persons the imprisoned fair was impressed upon her grandmother until it came really to this, that to keep her confined was almost as preposterous as her offence had been. There's no doubt that the freely expressed opinions of her son and her brother, John Botetort, had shaken the old gentlewoman; she as good as owned to herself that it would not do for Roddy to return and find his niece still in prison. But before she had been there much more than a week certain things occurred which made her enlargement a question of hours.

It seems, then, that she had been missed from the dinner-table after all by some of her acquaintance, and that my Lord Sandgate was one who had missed her. A week after her disgrace this gentleman, a widower of five years' standing, a man of substance and weight in the country, called upon Lady Morfa and asked leave in form to pay Miss Chambre his addresses. He frankly admitted that his acquaintance with her was slight and his resolution to improve it sudden. But if he was quick to make up his mind, he dared say that he was slow to change it. His political opinions were well known to her ladyship, and he was not without grounds of belief that Miss Chambre's coincided with them. He believed that the proposals he could make would be found perfectly satis-factory, had no doubt that he should be the most fortu-nate of men, and—paused for a reply. Such a serious offer made Lady Morfa serious. She promised to con-sider it; she told Lord Sandgate that she was flattered. It was not at all true, but she could hardly say less, knowing in her heart that it ought to be true. The man was a great gentleman and a weighty; Radical or not, he would assuredly be an earl. And when he left her, which he shortly did in a very dignified manner, she did consider him and his proposal together; and, though he got no benefit out of that, the girl did, for she had to be considered also. It became a pressing question whether an impertinence beyond belief was sufficient reason for shutting up a very possible peeress.

A few days later on another gentleman, ignorant of the first offer, came to woo. This was Tom Rodono, another Member of Parliament, another eldest son, a man of fashion and all the rest of it. Lady Morfa now felt that she was being made ridiculous; and that settled it.

Lord Rodono, when he was given to understand by Miss Harriet Moon that Hermia Mary was in disgrace, jumped at once to the nature of her offence. He remem-bered her look of fury at the dinner-party, when Mervyn Touchett dined his last at that table. "She's made a scene about Vernour. What a spirit! What a flame of a girl!" He knew that he was in love with her; he had known it for a long time; but he didn't guess how much he wanted her until he was told by Lady Morfa that it was out of the question. She was tolerant of him, good-humoured—for, after all, the proposal was not bad—and put on more manner than she generally affected. "My dear lord, your sentiments do you credit. Hermia is very much honoured—very much honoured, I am bound to say. But I must not disguise from you that I have other views—family interests, family claims, indeed—for the child. She is very young, quite unformed, and rather headstrong—that, no doubt, you have seen for yourself; and, of course, her education has not been all that one could wish. Her poor father—perhaps I need not speak of Colonel Chambre. You know my opinion upon subjects in which he—most unfortunately—poor man! But with regard to Hermia, you will forgive me if I don't mention this kind, this very honourable proposition of yours to her—let us say, for the present, at any rate. The child is not one-and-twenty until October, and is in my charge for another four years. Meantime, I trust so entirely in your discretion and—you will allow me?—good sense, that I hope we shall lose none of the intercourse which has been so pleasant, not only to Roderick and myself, but to Hermia also."

He had expected no less. "A thousand thanks, my lady," he said lightly. "No, I hope to see as much of

Caryll House as Caryll House will put up with. Don't be afraid that I shall go behind your authority, ma'am. That's not the way of it, I assure you."

"Of course, of course, my dear lord. I know with whom I have to deal." She was perfectly gracious to the poor gentleman—who felt more poorly than he cared to own. A waiting game, eh? He was in for a spell of Jacob's wooing. But that rascally Jacob permitted himself consolation which Lord Rodono now felt to be impossible for him. Five years for Hermia! Yes, but that glorious young creature to be kept five years! He knew his chance was of the slenderest. Meanwhile, where on earth had old Mother Morfa got her in ward?

He put in a word or two in mitigation of her supposed offence, spoke of his father and sister, who had fallen in love with her. "You might spare her to Grizel now and again, my lady. She'll be safe with her, I know, and be well out of this fly-blown town. No politics at Petersham, I promise you."

That was unlucky. Lady Morfa bristled, became bird-like. "Politics, Lord Rodono! Politics—and a child in her teens! No politics anywhere for my granddaughter, I can assure you."

"I'm with you there, my lady," said Rodono. "It's a grubby business for a lady's fingers." He had said more than he need, as he saw, and took leave. Coming out, he found Harriet close to the door, and made her jump.

"Ha, Miss Harriet, so I've caught you, have I?" He wasn't very fond of this young lady, and allowed himself to be blunt with her.

Miss Harriet put her hand to her side. "Oh, Lord Rodono, I was just——"

"I know you were, Miss Harriet; I know you were."

"I made sure that I heard her ladyship's bell. Indeed I——"

"Don't be afraid, my dear. I shan't bite—my teeth are drawn. Let me know if I can be of any use, though I believe you'll have Miss Hermy out before long, and you may tell her that I told you so."

"But I am not allowed to see her, Lord Rodono—and I don't know what it can have been." This must surely have been added for practice.

"Nor I, and I wish to heaven I did. I'll send Lady Grizel to her—but she'll be out in a day or two, I fancy." And away he went to his tilbury.

The two noble gentlemen, unconsciously rival, met in the House that warm afternoon, and yawned together upon the roomy benches of the Opposition. A dreary debate was in progress of the usual kind—of that kind which made Captain Ranald long for a pike, "to end the cackling and get something done." Mr. Percival was voicing his lamentations over some betrayal of "the generous instincts, the warm-hearted motions so creditable to his right honourable friend;" Lord Castlereagh was trimming his nails; Mr. Canning, showing his teeth, pretended a smile. The debts of Walcheren were massing, and soon must be met.

Lord Sandgate handed a *Weekly Register*, folded, to Rodono. "Seen that, Tom?" Rodono, his hat over his eyes, began to read languidly, but was soon keenly interested.

"An act of Carylldom has lately come to my notice, an act done to Mr. Vernour the butcher, of which I candidly confess I had not believed that precious house capable. But I was wrong, and offer my apologies— where they are due." Mr. Cobbett proceeded to nail down the facts—facts which we know. "Mr. Vernour, in the course of his business, one day last week received a visit from a personage—a young personage of high rank," etc.

He named no names, he was sedulously reserved. "This," he concluded, "I declare to be a royal act in the true sense of a word sadly out of season just now. And I will say rather, for that reason, that it is an heroic act, worthy of him who served his prisoner on his knees, great Edward's greater son. This, in fact, was an *uncommonly spirited affair*, conducted by the last Caryll in the world whom one could have thought had dared it. I could give a name if need were—but no! Let me learn from the act and the actors in it to emulate their own modesty; let nothing I may write infringe upon the sacred prerogative of youth, innocence, and beauty."

Rodono read that twice with heightened colour. It told him all.

Sandgate was watching him keenly. "Know who that is?" The other nodded. "It could only be one of them. Yes, yes, I know." And then he jerked his foot out, and let his head sink into his breast. "By heaven! I can't touch her hem! I'm not fit—" was his thought; but to Lord Sandgate he said, "You know that she could do it?"

Sandgate now nodded. "She could do more than that . . . and that old bitch-wolf has her locked up! . . . Cobbett must be told—I'll tell him. . . . By Gad, sir, we'll shame the old woman into honesty."

They resumed the subject at Brooks's. Lord Sandgate was for a meeting between Cobbett and Miss Chambre. "I should like to see her catch fire. By heaven, Tom, she could lead an army in the field—or to Windsor! We'll have our revolution yet."

Rodono declared himself. "I'm a victim. She's re-cruited me—but I shall have to wait. Mother Morfa won't look at me."

"Nor at me, damn her!" said his friend. Rodono looked up. "What, you too?"

"Yes," said Sandgate, "and I feel like wasting the world for a glance of her eyes." This grave gentleman, who sat nursing his leg, was very much in earnest. "It's a great game—to serve the like of her, Tom. She's got the air of a young Amazon—spoiling for it."

"War's in her blood, I'll allow you."

"And service in mine. To hold, as it were, her armour, hand it in piece by piece—the greaves, the cuisses, the breastplate and gorget. Picture her, sir, *cap-à-pie!* To gird on the sword, and put the spear in the young mailed hand!"

"Damn it, Sandgate, I'm with you there!"

"I'd like to run at her stirrup," said Lord Sandgate. "She's a Maid of Orleans—she's a Virgin-Saviour—she's one to die for! She's got eyes like a midsummer eve—eyes with fires dancing in 'em—eyes alight. To have seen her in that butcher's shop!"

Lord Rodono could not follow his friend so far. "No, no, Sandgate, keep her away from the mob. She's too fine for that. To have done it once—to show her mettle —that's enough. But lead her into this filthy trade we're at, she'll draggle. Cobbett—Cobbett and her!—is he man enough, gentleman enough?"

"She's a cut above gentlemen, my friend," said Lord Sandgate, very sure of himself; "she's got hands too fine for kid gloves. It's a man she must cope with—a man of ten thousand."

He grew excited; he rose and stood, back to the grate. "She shall meet Cobbett and all his men. She shall see old square-cut Cartwright — Burdett — Wolsely — old Tooke, the keen old spider. She shall see the lot, and hear 'em at their bloodiest. I'll back her. Let her be the test—if they pass through her fire, they're men.

She's of a rare breed—not a woman, but a flame! And now I'll go to bed."

"If she's not a woman, then it's certain that I'm not a man," said Rodono to himself. And back he too stalked to Park Place, where he lodged.

CHAPTER XV

TIME flies as the heart flies. Within six hours of the Act of Brook Street, Vernour and she, Brook Street itself and the whole wild incredible errand—the Resolve, which had been, as it were, the watching of the arms; the Dedication, when she rose that morning to her task; the Sally, the fulfilling of the Vow, the fiery ordeal of the Return—lay whole and composed, a legend, and a golden legend, in her memory. As she put by her arms she felt exceedingly complacent that her task was smoothly done. It had been difficult, more difficult than she had expected; she did not stay to examine why—all she knew at this first blush of release was that she had triumphed. She had been loyal—so she put it—to her traditions; she had kept alive in her own breast the flame which her father had kindled there. She had championed the Rights of Man.

Very much excited, her mind alert, her imagination flying high and far, she flitted to and fro, traversing her little kingdom of two rooms a thousand times. Her thoughts just now were entirely pious; she remembered her father without mourning him any more; her gentle mother, too, to whom every whim of her husband's had

been a law. She remembered how fine had been Lady
Hermione's loyal acceptance of the democratic faith;
she remembered, for instance—and it didn't seem in the
least ridiculous—that she had tried to be "Citizen Hermione," as the colonel was Citizen Chambre, and had
only given it up because it was so extremely difficult to
say. Another trouble had been that the peasantry would
have nothing to do with such freaks of naming; her
father had always been "the Cornel's Honour," and her
mother "My lady." There had been a time—no more
than a week ago—when Hermia would have laughed, say
with Tom Rodono, over these things; but now, swiftly
roaming her prison, she thought them splendid. They
made her heart beat. When she caught sight of her own
face, as she passed the looking-glass, she hardly knew
herself in this eager, flushed War-Maid, whose grey
eyes shone like jet, whose lips were parted and hair
streaming free. In the glow and fervency of her
thoughts she wrote—standing to do it—to Mary Fox:
and how her pen raced over the sheet! . . . "I am
perfectly satisfied I have done right. Don't seek to
persuade me otherwise, Mary—scold me if you like, but
no sophisms. I have been living these last few hours
with papa and mamma—I have seen them as plain as I
see this paper. They look kindly at me, their eyes
smile—they would stroke my hair, and papa would kiss
me, if they weren't ghosts. I have heard again, with
perfect distinctness, dear papa's favourite paradox—

Always be proud enough to be humble, my Hermy. I am sure that I have pleased him. I don't care what happens to me now."

She left her letter here because that last half-phrase had struck her as so curiously true that she had to consider it. She walked about again, stood at the windows—that of her bedroom, which gave on to the walled garden; that of her boudoir, which showed her the courtyard in front, the statue of Earl Rupert, the locked gates, and the lodge. And it was at this latter window that she made a discovery. She found herself blushing and trembling: very slightly, it's true, but trembling she was, and blushing—and extremely happy. Why was this? What had happened? She stayed her researches into her own thoughts; she left her questions unanswered—but she did not cease to put them.

The legend was rehearsed, that golden legend—step by step to Brook Street, step by step of the return. But there was a noticeable hiatus. She always skipped the scene with Vernour where she had passed under his arm into the little parlour, and where she had felt that most peculiar sensation of being a bird fluttering under a hand. She approached it always in her thought with high beating of the heart; but then she closed her eyes and felt herself burning, and lost herself in the fire— and when she came to herself again, she was either talking of the Clanranald family to Mrs. Vernour or speeding homewards, or confronted with grandmamma. There

was a fierce kind of excitement in this gradual, conscious
approach to a forbidden moment, in the tiptoe venture
to the very edge, in the peep too long, the slip, the slide
downwards to the fiery flood, the momentary drowning;
and then there was the relief of recovery, and the sense
of danger past. She lived it over and over again; time
existed no longer. She conned her legend until she had
it by heart, until she knew the perilous passages of it,
and could judge whether she was capable of reviewing
them, or must not. . . . If she indulged herself, if she
nursed her wound, it's no wonder. What else was she to
do? Her heart was, as it were, in her arms, against her
bosom. She fondled it. This must be confessed. . . .
It was all very secret, very sweet, very foolish and, be-
like, very wrong, . . . but if outraged grandmammas
lock up fair impertinents as a punishment for temerity,
this is the sort of penance the prisoners will perform.

I don't see why I should make any mystery about a
very simple matter. David Vernour, seen by Miss
Chambre for a second of time on that day in January
when she first came to the home of her race, had by this
end of April assumed the proportions of a hero. It may
be granted that he had himself done nothing towards it,
if it is granted in return that he had done nothing
against it. But to grant me that return is to grant me the
whole position. It does so happen that in the few moments
when he was face to face with the visionary he had
carried himself with simplicity and dignity. If he was

no hero, he had not been unheroic.   Indeed, it is difficult
to see what better a hero himself could have done.   Everything else had been the young lady's work.   She had
spun the mist through which he loomed like the Brocken-
shadow, enormous and god-like; she had lent the fire
which ruddied the dream; by every effort of hers he
had gained; and every new wrong done him by the
Carylls had seemed a new virtue in the victim of their
spleen.   And not only he, but his family, partook this
glamour.   The Brook Street establishment became a
sanctuary, the Brook Street denizens patriarchs.   It had
never—even in the first moment of reality—entered her
head to say, "These people are not as I am."   She was
too much her father's child, and too much the child of her
enthusiastic generation for that to be possible.   Nothing
had offended her, nothing jarred.   The men in frocks
and aprons, the woman with hands pink and soft from
the wash-tub—she had noticed nothing amiss.   She had
been full of her errand, swept along by it; and now that
it was all over, and she was so triumphantly right, so
sure that she had done well—now there was no question
of reality at all.   David Vernour shone through his blue
frock like Apollo through his shepherd-skins—what time
he was keeping herds for Admetus, serving his term in
proud humility with that Thessalian king.

Her seclusion was rigid, and might have been irksome.
No one was admitted to her but Moth; and what Moth
may have surmised she was too discreet to exhibit.   But

for the first day or two this black-eyed, demure young
woman was entirely at a loss to know who "he" might be.
It was, of course, obvious that the situation involved a
man. If families and persons filled Lady Morfa's world,
Moth's contained two classes also—expectant woman and
advancing man. Was it Lord Rodono? Was it Mr.
Touchett? She could put two and two together, and
had heard of that gentleman's performance at the dinner-table; it had gone to swell the great horse-question
which had been canvassed in the housekeeper's room with
far more freedom than elsewhere. Parties were equally
divided down there; the Jacob Jacobs of the gold-laced
hat and black stockings was not quite the same man one
might have seen in slippered ease with Mrs. James, with
Mr. Progers, and my lord's own man. Mrs. James, the
housekeeper, was strongly on the Family side; so was
her ladyship's woman, Mrs. Elkington. Moth, on the
other hand, was for Vernour, whose charms of person
demanded sympathy, and she hailed his return to the
tradesman's door with tender interest. Jacob Jacobs
did not disguise that he respected the young butcher,
and that he cared not who knew it. It is true that he
had been scandalised by that shocking encounter; but it
is also true that he had been impressed by it. For
although to lay hands upon a peer is a sacrilegious act,
yet to have done so, and not to have been blasted, entitles
you to the esteem of your fellow-men. Vernour still lived,
and again plied his trade at Caryll House. This was in

itself a career. So a truly religious man might feel towards one who had successfully robbed a church. But neither Jacobs nor Moth had an inkling of the present state of the case. Moth had, in fact, finally decided for Touchett.

Meantime, on the third day of her imprisonment, Miss Chambre discovered that half-past ten in the morning was the hour of David Vernour's appearance before the gates of Caryll House; and on the fourth that he was aware of her. This was an act of divination on her part, for on his he never once let her know it. It was as he was tethering his horse, or talking with Jacobs at the gates, that he looked towards the window where she sat; once inside the court, although he had to cross immediately under it, he kept his eyes to the ground; nor did he look at her again until he was once more at the horse's head. She was very much puzzled to know how he had learned of her confinement, but assumed that he had guessed it. She saw him every day so long as she remained a prisoner, and nothing could have kept her from the window. When she was released at the end of the week, and free of the house and grounds, on the contrary, nothing in the world would have brought her to the gates at half-past ten in the morning.

But here, in the middle of London, were all the conditions of an Italian novel: a window and a secluded lady, a confidential maid, a young man whose business led him daily by the house. The action should have flowed naturally; the lady should lean over the balcony and one day drop a flower; the maid should hear her complaint, and one day confide it to the lover below; notes should pass, and all the rest be in a concatenation. Nothing of the kind here. The romance endured with the imprisonment and ceased the moment it became easier of fruition; and as for the notes, they came and went by the post.

He wrote to her, but after her release, "I beg Miss Chambre to believe that no word from me has occasioned the paragraph in the newspaper. I beg her to do me this act of justice, and to believe me with the greatest respect her obliged servant, D. VERNOUR."

She did not hesitate to reply: "DEAR SIR: I have seen no paragraphs, but had I seen them, should never have supposed them yours. In any case, I should have been very indifferent to them. I remain, dear sir, yours, much obliged, HERMIA MARY CHAMBRE."

She was released, as I say, after a week, and left her rooms to all appearances her natural self. How far that was true I don't, at this stage of her history, take it upon me to say. Her visions ceased with the opportunity of dreaming, and she sought no more material—indeed, she was careful to avoid it. She never left the house or returned to it between half-past ten and a quarter to eleven; and she did not pay another call upon Mrs. Vernour. So much Harriet Moon ascertained—who, for her part, had no scruples about her hours for going out and coming in.

CHAPTER XVI

WHEN Lady Morfa, under stress of the thought that
she was keeping in ward a person for which two
eldest sons of earls had asked within a few days of each
other, released her granddaughter, she knew that she was
committed to her last expedient. Unless you are a Catho-
lic—with walled convents in the background—there is
really no middle course. If you cannot keep a handsome
young lady at home, and dare not let her abroad, you
must marry and be done with her. She is not a specimen
for a museum, after all. Miss Chambre, at any rate, did
not appear to consider herself so; but, being enlarged,
came forth no whit abashed, said her "Good-morning,
grandmamma," very happily, and stooped a fresh, if
somewhat pale, cheek to be kissed. Without any desire
to blink regrettable facts, she complained of want of
exercise, and demanded a horse and squire. The mar-
riage-treaty must be faced.

But the marriage of a Caryll by the mother's side is no
light matter—no common affair of instinct and heart-
ache. There are high contracting parties to such a
marriage, and settlements and minute precautions for the

proper maintenance of offspring. That which you would blush to remember in the case of Jack and Jill, here you would blush to forget. In a certain sense it is almost vulgar that such an alliance should be opened by a gentleman with a heart-complaint; it is surely better that the authorities should sound each other, the land-agents having been consulted, and the powers verified. Certainly, Lords Sandgate and Rodono had not advanced their suits by the methods adopted; in any case, they were ineligible. The Codnor properties were in the west, the Drem estate was miserably cut into by jointures, and was Scotch at the best. There remained Lord Edlogan to consider, son of the Duke of Wentsland and Bryng-win—desirable in every way—but she held him over for the present, and, like a king in a crisis, sent for Sir George Coigne.

This young baronet of Bucks, summoned by his aunt to form an administration, arrived punctually to the minute, driving his four bays from Plashetts as became so famous a whip. "From Uxbridge under the hour, ma'am, upon my soul; two hours and fifty-five minutes from Wendover Cross—and going like clockwork!" He was a prosperous young man, uniformly cheerful; he was sandy, red-faced, wholesome, and slim, very neat in the leg. In addition to his coachmanship, which was his great art, he was a certain shot at a woodcock, a keen farmer, not above racing; he had been seen at more than one mill, backing his fancy man, and could put out a main of cocks for a battle at two days' notice. These were his occupations, pursued with the kind of zest most men have for their diversions. In addition, he owned a borough, always at the service of the Opposition, and a comfortable fifteen thousand a year, all in land. Although he was turned thirty, he had never considered marriage, for (as he explained) with horses and hounds a man's hands are pretty full. He bred both, and had taken prizes. But Lady Morfa was fully sure of him. His mother had never allowed him to forget that she had been a Botetort. The Coignes, of course, were respectable, but no more: an old county family. The baronetcy dated from George II.

Her ladyship came to the point with more than her accustomed precision—with more, because she was dealing with a kinsman, to whom a preface would have been impertinent. Her very first words were really a compliment to Family. "Now, George," she said, "I've found a match for you; and you must be extremely sensible and listen to me."

"Always do that, aunt—do me the justice," says Sir George, looking at his Hessians. Had he been a common person, you would have sworn that he had whistled as he heard the first words.

"It's Hermia Chambre," said Lady Morfa; "good blood on both sides, as I am bound to own. I never approved of Dick Chambre, perhaps I need not say—but, after all, he might have been worse. If, for instance, he had not run away with poor Hermione, I doubt if any-body else would. And he would certainly have had all Ireland by the ears if he could have kept quiet. But he set up for a wit, poor man—must talk. Heavens! I can hear him now with his, 'Mark me, madam, a man is not a dumb beast.' He did his best to prove that. He was green wood—all smoke and splutter; but I have never denied his birth. *That* he had, though I dare say he was heartily ashamed of it. As to Hermia, you know she has nothing of her own—five hundred a year, or something of the kind—but I shall see to that. She's been with me now since Christmas, and I certainly like her, I must say. She's a beauty, I suppose—too full for perfection, per-haps—too mature; but the fault's on the right side, and——"

"Quite so, quite so," Sir George murmured to his boots, and wondered what might come next.

"She made a great effect when I brought her out—very gratifying. There was a time when I thought that the Pr——; but, however—nothing came of that."

"Good Lord! no," said the vexed Sir George. "Too bad."

"She's full of spirit," her ladyship calmly pursued, "can answer you like a wit at a dinner-table. I know she has courage, though I think she is obstinate and perverse. But that is because she has been brought up anyhow. A year's training will work wonders—and, of course, there's no hurry. What is she? Twenty, I suppose—barely that."

"Ought to take 'em early, aunt, eh?" said Sir George, his mind's eye now roaming over his walled paddocks, where slim chestnuts grazed at ease.

"Well, now, George, I must tell you that she's been greatly admired. The Duke of Sussex said to me—well, you know the kind of thing those creatures say. Their compliments, my dear! They talk like salesmen! But I've had two proposals for her—one excellent in many ways, and I've reason to know that the Duke's son has had a thought of her. If it were not for a most unfortunate occurrence in which she chose to *embroil* herself—but the other, I'll tell you in confidence, was Lord Sandgate. Lord Sandgate, the friend of—that man! My dear George Coigne, I don't wish to flatter you—but between you and Lord Sandgate what choice have I?"

She paused, and her nephew had to take up the tale. Alarmed as he had been, disturbed, and, as he expressed it, "put about," he was by no means at the end of his tether yet. Talk of this sort amused women, and women amused him, so long as they didn't get too close. His aunt was got as close as he cared about, but he thought that careless interest, so to speak, might serve his turn best. Could he not hint the dawning of an idea? Yes, yes, but how the deuce do you do that kind of thing? The old lady was serious, and might take him up short if he was not careful—and talking was such infernal nonsense. One of the few trials of his life was the having to say what he wanted, instead of to get it. It is probable that his natural manner, which was unemotional, jerky, and genial at once, helped him in this uncomfortable pass, for it did combine, rather happily, brusquerie and compliment. It should certainly be a great compliment to your partner in a conversation that you take compliments as a matter of course.

He thumbed his waistcoat, stretched his fine legs to the full, cleared his throat, and settled into his stock. "My dear aunt, I take this very kindly in you—upon my life, very kindly indeed. I don't know what I can say, except that, of course, I'd never thought of Hermy Chambre— in that sort of way, you know. Nice gal—fine gal—well set up—rides uncommonly straight, eh?"

This did not take him far.

"I'm told she rides excellently," said her ladyship, and left it there for him.

"Hardly know her, you know—eh?" Sir George continued, hammering upon his manner. "Full of breed and all that—full of go and pace—fine action and all that, eh? Family first rate, of course—very young, though—what?"

"Virgin soil," said Lady Morfa; "virgin soil."

Sir George jumped as though he had been shot, and immediately perceived that that made it worse. Really, his aunt was—eh? But he hastened now to agree. "Not a doubt of it—oh, of course, of course! My dear aunt!

Very charming and all that." Exquisitely uncomfortable, he felt that no praise from him could be too strong for a lady whom his aunt could so exhibit. "Yes, upon my soul, I always liked the gal—little Miss Hermy— eh?" This was further than he had meant to go, but his aunt had shocked him. Virgin soil—oh, damn it!

"Very well," said the lady, "then I suppose that we know where we are."

"Eh?" said he. "Oh, well, aunt, we won't drive her, you know. Never do with a youngster. She'd shy off to a certainty. No, we must go slower than that. I'll turn it over—turn it over in my mind, you know. We've time enough, as I think you said—we must go slow."

"It was you who said so," observed her ladyship, "not I."

"Oh, well, after all, you know—there *is* plenty of time." His discomfort turned him at bay. "I must really—you'll forgive me, aunt—I must really do some serious thinking here, and consideration, eh? Put on my considering cap, and all that, you know." He paused blankly, and felt constrained to qualify what had sounded to him horribly crude. "But she's a fine gal—stout, trim gal—rare colour and all that." She might have been a wine. "So now I think—" He rose.

"Think of it, George; that's all I ask," said Lady Morfa, not truthfully, and gave him her hand, which he kissed before he left the presence. At the door he sighed his immense relief. "God Almighty, I thought she'd got me!"

In the corridor, down which he stroke briskly, manhood returning at every step, he came suddenly upon Harriet Moon, who, with bent head, seemed to be hurrying about her business. We now find a very different Sir George Coigne—one of quickened colour and assured gallantry.

"God bless me, it's Miss Moon!" She looked up like a startled roe, but almost immediately showed him her long lashes.

"Oh, Sir George, I—" Her hand, which was a very small one, felt like a caught mouse in his.

"Upon my life, Miss Harriet, I'm very glad to see you again. I do hope you're very well."

"Yes, thank you, Sir George."

"One never sees you here nowadays. You've been missed, I can tell you."

"I was just going to her ladyship, Sir George, when——"

"Yes, I know—I'm in luck's way. Let's see, how long is it since you were at Plashetts?"

"Nearly six months," said Harriet quickly and accurately.

"By Gad, is it so long?" She had regained her hand. "I say, Miss Harriet, do you remember the skewbald? And how frightened you were?"

"Yes, indeed, Sir George."

"I shall never forget that myself so long as I live in

this wicked world," said the baronet. "You took my arm, you know. But you've forgiven me, haven't you?"

"Oh, surely, Sir George."

"You know I wouldn't do you any—you know that I think very much of your—good looks, eh?" This was a new Sir George, unknown to his aunt. Miss Moon had nothing to say, and her cast-down eyes moved him strongly. He was bound to see them.

"Miss Harriet—oh, Harriet—" She looked up, pleadingly, beautifully, tearfully, and in another moment her hands were caught—and what might have occurred thereupon if Hermia had not then entered the corridor— Hermia, fresh from her ride—one does not know. That is what happened; Harriet flew. "Oh, how d'ye do, Hermy?" said Sir George to his proffered bride.

"Quite well, thank you, George," said she. "What have you been doing to poor Harriet?"

Poor Harriet! The contrast between his own state and that of the divinely dowered Harriet tempted him to chuckle. "I was just telling Miss Moon, you know, she must really bring you down to Plashetts. This weather— we're at our best—with the grass beginning to grow— and all that. And flowers! Do you like flowers? We've any quantity of flowers. I do think you'd be pleased with us; I do indeed. You go and stay with old Drem— I know you do, because Lady Grizel told me—and it's not fair, you know. Now, really, when will you come down?"

"You must ask grandmamma," says she. "She has me body and soul."

"Oh, no, by George!" He was knowing. "Not she! Don't tell me that. You have a way of your own, I believe. And Tom Rodono says so."

"You collect your information from that family? I don't think he knows much about me."

Sir George mused. Tom was the man! That might be captained by an artful one. "Good fellow, Tom," he said, "but he's idle, you know; wants looking after. But, mind you, he's a man you may depend upon—so long as he don't get angry. Never let him get angry."

"Really!" said Miss Chambre. "What have I to do with his passions?" He was going too fast. Damn it, he was making a mess of the thing.

"Oh, quite so, quite so. What have you? No, no— that's absurd. But about your visit to Plashetts now. I do hope you'll think of that."

"It's very kind of you, George. I'll see."

"Do—pray do. Now I must be off. County meeting at Amersham this evening. Reform, and all that. I promised I'd go. Waysford asked me. Must keep up, you know, eh?"

"Yes, I hope you'll keep up," says she. "We expect it of you."

"By George, we're all Whigs here, I know—but Reform! I'll tell you this, Hermy, between you and me and the doorpost. I don't much like it. That little place of mine, you know—Condover—well, that'd go, you know. Three freeholders besides myself—and one's my bailiff, and the other's his son, and the other's the woodman. Now, what I say is, that's mine, you know—my grandfather bought it—paid for it. But there you are—I said I'd go, and I will go. And you're quite right about keeping up—that's sport, that is. Well, by-by, Hermy." They touched hands. He added, "I say, though, I do think I'd bring Miss Moon with you—to Plashetts, I mean. My mother likes her."

She laughed. "Oh, of course, I understand that I should be valueless without——"

"Not at all! Only too charmed to have you anyhow—what? Lucky to get you, I know. But Miss Moon—she's useful, you know—been there before, knows the ways, and all that. I do think I'd bring her, if I were you."

"I shall certainly bring her," said Hermia. "Good-bye, Cousin George."

When she found her friend, she said nothing of Sir George or his proposals, but talked of indifferent things—and then, suddenly, she looked at Harriet, who was very aware of it, and put her arm round her waist, and kissed her. Harriet, after a proper moment of surprise, embraced her with both arms, and kissed her back. Nothing was said by them—and nothing need have been said by me, but that I think the little incident marks a step in Miss Chambre's sentimental education.

"Moon I believe to be sly," her ladyship had said upon one occasion, and was no doubt right.   But the question is, How is a little thin daughter of nobody to keep her soul her own unless she use the only weapon she has—a pair of melting brown eyes and a fine curtain of lashes over them?   These, and a pretty, deferential way, were, so far as I can see, all her simple armoury.   To be sure, there was religion; but it had not come to that yet.

CHAPTER XVII

WHICH EXPOUNDS A NEW USE FOR ONE'S MISTRESS

MY Lord Viscount Sandgate was an enthusiast of that
dangerous sort which can turn all things human
and divine to his single purpose, to which nothing is too
sacred for use, or fails to get, as it gives, colour and
radiance by use. If he was a lover, his love must be so
much capital for his ventures; if he was an adventurer,
his ventures must be sanctified by his love. He would
have said, My mistress is my pole-star, and I walk in
her beam. Yes, but I travel to the pole. The pole of
his endeavour was assuredly Revolution, the lantern for
his feet of French make. Into this lantern, as a guide
for this end, he proposed to place the enkindled heart of
the fair Chambre.

He was not one of those politicians who can plod; he
was vehement and importunate of Fortune. Reform,
which had promised so fair in the days of '94, now
seemed to him mere patchwork, scarcely worth his while.
At best it was but a handle to the axe he longed to wield;
and as time went on, and ministers sat immovable in
their places, and the Opposition rootedly asleep in its
constitutional fortress, my Lord Sandgate began to
pant for the open, and to snatch at any handles he

could find. It must be admitted that he was not squeamish. If Colonel Wardle and the Cyprian of Gloucester Place gave him no qualms, who or what could? He had used these not too cleanly levers so long as they would serve; and after them Mr. Reding, the broker of seats. With the purchased lady he had belaboured the honour of a royal duke, with the gentleman bruised Lord Castlereagh's heel—and so far, good. Now, as it seemed to him, he had the opportunity of striking deeper. Corruption, when all was said, was but a surface sore; Privilege was a cancer. You must excise that with a knife. Now, suppose that he could inspire his friends with some of the enthusiasm which he had felt for Miss Chambre's gallant deed—suppose, even, that he could egg on that brilliant young leveller to greater havoc—had he not a knife wherewith to slice Privilege? He certainly thought so.

Remember, he was in love with this lady. She imaged for him the live flame of chivalry, that altar-fire which he could not believe extinguished altogether, and without which he could not hope for any ordered universe. If he chiefly admired her wit and franchise, her high spirits, he was not at all insensible to her beauty, and was clear as to the extraordinary value of her noble birth. He promised himself the raptures of possession as heartily as Tom Rodono or any ordinary man could ever have done, but flattered himself with the vision of a rarer joy—when they two with level breasts should lead the forces of Liberty into battle, and sit, still side by side, enthroned upon the wreck of kings. The picture is confused—for what have thrones to do with Liberty, unless everybody is to have a throne? But it pleased him when he made it; it gave zest to his efforts when he set about his design of a meeting between his Phrygian goddess, as he strangely called her, and his ally, the stout Mr. Cobbett.

Nothing could have needed contrivance more nice, but he pursued the plan with such ardour that he was able to manage it towards the middle of June. While Lord Castlereagh was nursing his honour and Mr. Canning his thirst for blood; while the troops in Walcheren were rotting of dysentery and Sir Arthur Wellesley was pushing on towards the massacre at Talavera; while the Prince was getting rid of Mrs. Fitzherbert and Mr. Croker advising Lord Hertford in a very delicate affair, the hospitable Lady Burdett invited Miss Chambre to dine, go to the play, and spend the night at her house in Piccadilly. No opposition was raised by the authorities, nor any expectation in Hermia's breast. It seemed a very ordinary kind of festivity.

She thought the dinner-party decorous and a little dull. Lord Sandgate was present, no doubt, and she admired him as a spectacle and as a force. He was a tall, slim, aquiline man in those days, inclining to middle age, hopelessly an aristocrat. What interested her about him was to see how he could turn not only his judgment and wit, but his fine manner and a hundred prejudices also, to the service of his convictions. He was credited with fire, and she knew that he could act with energy—as when he had pulled her back by the gown at a dangerous moment for her; but where did he hide his fire? Outwardly, he was grave and silent; must he not lack warmth, passion, ardour? Our young lady, who lacked certainly none of these, and had, moreover, full measure of the Irish critical sense, judged him rather a tragical object for the Reformer's ranks. He handed her in to dinner; but love was no more able than patriotism to break down his reserve. He added nothing to the success of the party. Lord Rodono and his sister did better; Mrs. Wing and Mr. Engayne, long lovers, did as little as they could. Lady Burdett, very amiable, but rather helpless, exhausted her powers in praising Hermia's beauty; every few minutes she fell into a vague rapture, called her "lovely creature," and recovered. Sir Francis, one of the handsomest men of his day, and one of the most popular, held himself in reserve. No politics were discussed, and at seven o'clock the ladies, with two young men in attendance, went to the play, the other gentlemen to the House of Commons.

On returning to supper the scene was changed. The long reception rooms were brilliant; in the end one of all, through open doors was to be seen a round table, covered with silver and glass. It had as a centre-piece a curious, tall gilt ornament which represented a throne upon degrees. Behind that stood a lamp-post—a *lan-*

terne—with its swinging lamp upon the fatally sugges-
tive arm; upon the top of all this imagery was perched
a red Phrygian cap made of silk, and made evidently
to be worn.   What did this "poetry" mean?   Tom
Rodono, who vowed he was not in the secret, had no
notion.   Miss Chambre, interested as she was, excited
and lively, had none; and the man, for his part, cared
little what she had or had not, so long as he could look
at her.   She was looking beautiful, there's no doubt, in
her white silk gown, with her glowing colour and dark
masses of hair.   Her eyes, it has before been observed,
had the property of seeming black at night.   They were
grey, in fact, but at night, when she was excited, they
filled up with black, and gleamed like jewels.   Sapphires
have the same virtue.

Three guests were expected, and no more.   One of
them she knew and was glad to see.   Captain Ranald, brisk
and spruce, made her his best bow, and seemed to pick
up his intercourse where he had left it three months ago.
He was fresh from the sea, had left Brest Roads but a
fortnight ago, landed at Southampton yesterday, trav-
elled all night, made a scene in the House of Commons
that afternoon, and here he was.   "What are we all about
here?   Burdett told me nothing but that I should have
the pleasure of meeting you again.   I have heard great
things of you."

She blushed and smiled.   "And did you know that I
have heard of you, too?"

"No, indeed. You will hear little good of me in London, from what I can gather."

"But mine was all good. It was from Mrs. Vernour."

"Ah! Yes, indeed. And her praise is worth having. What on earth have we here?"

The butler had announced "Mr. Hunt," and Lady Grizel had put up her glasses to inspect the owner of so unremarkable a name. A florid gentleman, who bowed too low and too often, and seemed afflicted with excessive heat in the region of the temples, was now in the room; but why he was there, or on whose bidding, was not apparent. It was probably on Lord Sandgate's. He plunged almost immediately into political discussion, and spoke of a Reform meeting at Salisbury as if it had been one of the Six Days of Creation. Shortly afterwards, the butler entered again with a huge man at his heels, broad-shouldered, bluff, and very conscious of his powers. It was hardly necessary for him to be called "Mr. Cobbett"—he was his own best herald. Here, at any rate, was somebody worth study—a leader of the people and a force in the land. Miss Hermia devoured him with her fine eyes.

He was very much at his ease, and not ungainly in his free-spoken way. He kissed his hostess's hand, clapped that of Sir Francis; had a joke for Ranald, a bow for Rodono, and two or three words in a half whisper for Lord Sandgate. Of Mr. Hunt he took no notice whatever, but stood, after his first salutations, surveying the

ladies—meditating upon them, as if they had been
flowers in his garden-plot, with not unpleasant satisfaction. Miss Hermia could not but think that his hands
were too deep in his breeches' pockets, his feet too far
apart and too firmly planted. Although it was midsummer, he stood back to the fire, a coat-tail under each
arm; and although it was near midnight, he still wore
cords and boots. She was ashamed of herself for notic-
ing such things, when better things were at hand—for
instance, Lord Sandgate's respect for his opinion, and a
fine benevolence twinkling in his sharp eyes and creasing
his wholesome face. Presently, to her confusion, the man
started and looked at his interlocutor. "God bless me!
You don't tell me that, my lord!" he said, and crossed
the room to where she stood. He waited for no formali-
ties, but exclaiming as he came, "Let me see face to face
the most honest girl in England," had her hand in his
in a trice; took and kept it in his own huge paw. She
was blushing hotly, but that became her very well. "My
dear young lady, you are an honour to your sex. I've
three fine sons at home who, but for the grace of God,
might any one of them have been in Vernour's shoes—or
frock; and I know what your act would have done for
him. You've exercised the privilege of your sex; you've
made a man, my dear. I declare that I should like to
give you the best I have in me to give, and that's the
salute of an honest fellow." He looked at her so benevolently as he said it, so comically, that she laughed.

"You will make me very proud, sir."

"Why, then," said he, "pride for ever!" and kissed her fairly. "And now, my lady," he turned to Lady Burdett, "let me hand you to your own supper-table." This he prepared to do without any more ceremony; but when he found that she chose to go last, he stood aside with good humour, and kept her hand upon his arm with an insistence not to be mistaken. Sir Francis led the way with Hermia Mary, who now began to perceive that she was the guest of the evening.

The party was a noisy one, more boisterous than merry. Mr. Cobbett talked the whole time; and so did Mr. Hunt. They talked against each other. Bob Ranald was the only perfectly happy person present; Lord Rodono was sulky. He now had a suspicion of what was to come. All this was, of course, Sandgate's doing, and be damned to him. "Look, I ask you," he said to Mrs. Wing, "look at the demiurgic rascal, who has dragged us all here, and wound us up, and now proposes to sit still while we jig for his amusement. You may say what you please of Miss Hermia's performance—and I, for one, rate it highly. I was like going down on my knees to her when it was done; but that fellow over there sees in it so much capital. He's an usurious dog—and we shall be well out of this party with our shirts on our backs. Hunt! Regard Hunt! He's over-drinking himself. What have we done to be treated like this by Jack Sandgate—and in another man's house, if you please! That's a particular beauty of it all."

Midway through the meal there came a lull in the talk—or debate, as it was now become; and in that lull a rather terrible divergence was caused by Mr. Hunt. He leaned over the table, with a solemn expression upon his face. "Miss Chambre—Madam—the honour of a glass of wine with you," she heard. Mr. Ranald looked at the ceiling, Rodono at his own folded arms; but Sir Francis supplied her glass, and the thing was done. Mr. Hunt was for enlarging upon the theme, but happily could not. The talk flowed over him again and drowned him; Ranald returned to his sea-stories and Cobbett to forestry; Lord Sandgate watched his puppets jig, and Sir Francis sat urbane, smiling and quiet—meditating, probably, his immediate task.

In the next lull this fine gentleman, who never failed to do a thing well, however little he may have relished it, rose and made the company a speech. He said that, honoured as he was by the presence of undoubted patriots at his table, he must be permitted to observe that all alike were honoured by the presence of one so young and so intrepid, so diligent to hold the narrow path of honour as the charming lady who came among them to claim her right to alliance in the cause. He need not relate the circumstances, which were fresh in all their minds, under which this lady showed her mettle. They were, he must confess, peculiarly adapted for that display, being of a nature which might well have daunted one less nobly equipped. The forces of prestige, high rank, and influence were not alone arrayed against her; nearer and more invincible forces were brought up to aid them. Single-handed she faced the host, single-handed she showed that no privilege, however chartered, no influence, howsoever founded, could prevail against honour. He would not despair of England, of the Commonwealth, nor of that Reform to which they were all pledged, while such devotion existed in the breast of a young, highly born, and beautiful lady. The Rights of Man were grounded on reason, religion, and justice. It was due to the piety of woman that they had never been nearer their recognition than they were now in this year, 1809. He asked his friends to join with him in welcoming Miss Chambre to that society, founded by the glorious youth of Horne Tooke, cemented by the pains of John Thelwall, that society of which he was proud to be a member—the Society of the Friends of the People.

Lord Sandgate sprang to his feet. Nobody had ever seen him so moved. "Madam," he said with warmth, "I salute in your person Divine Compassion!" and there stopped; then Mr. Hunt must needs follow him with a "God bless you, Miss Chambre," but Cobbett pulled him down by the coat-tails. "Divine Compassion is good, my Lord Sandgate," said that worthy, "but Divine Right is better—and here's the emblem of it." With that, he

picks the crimson cap off its lamp-post and, coming behind her chair, sets it upon Miss Hermia's head. The
burning thing rested upon its dark nest, for all the world
like the sun of winter setting into a bank of cloud. The
whole company rose and faced her; her health was given
with three times three amid tumultuous applause, in the
course of which Mr. Hunt broke three wine-glasses; and
after that, and concerning all that, one at least at the
table felt that the less said the better. He had kept his
eyes upon the girl, and saw that she was not far from
tears. It came upon him on a certain wave of disgust
that she might really be gratified at this extraordinary
and most unfortunate tribute. And, as everybody concerned seemed to be forgetting himself, so did Lord
Rodono, probably, when he rose to his feet.

"Sir Francis, ladies and gentlemen," he said, "I believe
Miss Chambre would desire me to thank you for the
compliment you have paid her." He was here reassured
by a grateful glance, and went on. "She is one of those,
in my belief, who chooses to do her fine things in her
own way and to say little about them. The less, indeed,
the better. I do nothing to diminish the value of your
compliment when I assert that her good deeds were never
published by herself or by the object of them. And I
hope I may add that she will be best served and most
honoured if her fame goes no further than these walls.
She is not one whose charity should be blazed about
Piccadilly."

"But it should, my lord," Cobbett struck in, "and it shall—if the sound of it can reach Carlton House."

Tom Rodono looked very bleak. "Then, Mr. Cobbett, a wrong will be done—and in spite of the lady's friends. Among the sticks with which you beat your dogs, you shall not, by our leave, include Miss Chambre."

"She has numbered herself," Cobbett thundered, "she has numbered herself. She has whipped Privilege across the chops, and we have dealt a cut for liberty this night which is worth a score of divisions, and ten score of county meetings. Ah!" he cried to her, "ah, my noble young lady, you little thought when you achieved your act of grace that the rebound could carry it hissing over England!" After that, while Rodono was down, very angry and biting his cheek, Mr. Cobbett held the floor. He spoke of Vernour well and eloquently, if one could have cared to hear about the man just now; but the more he said, the worse he made it. The note was a false one, the emphasis made it shrieking-false; it was like a man singing flat and holding the note. Even Sir Francis had had enough of it, and whispered behind Lady Grizel to Sandgate—for God's sake to pull him down. But that was easier said than done, and Lord Sandgate took no notice. What he had done he had done—*cosa fatta capo ha*. So Cobbett harped away unhindered: "That sturdy young fellow—that fine, manly, English fellow—a judge of a horse, a very Centaur, my friends—hounded into gaol," etc., etc. He might have gone on for ever but for Mr. Hunt, of Wiltshire.

Mr. Hunt, very red and excited, here jumped to his feet and claimed the auditory. He got it by a sudden bang on the table which made Cobbett start. "I declare," he said resonantly, "I declare that the honest fellow's wrongs touch my heart. I beg to propose, therefore, a public subscription for a testimonial of respect to David Vernour, and shall be pleased to put my name down for fifty guineas."

The thing was getting quite horrible, but yet there was no moving Lord Sandgate. It was neck or nothing with him; he would have been the first to say that if you go in on the Radical side you mustn't wear thin shoes. Sir Francis would have stopped it if he could; or Ranald, if he had not feared to make it worse. As for Rodono— "Damn you, Sandgate, damn you, damn you!" he groaned to himself.

There being no reply from any of these gentlemen, Mr. Hunt's proposal fell flat; and then Cobbett crushed it to powder.

"Pooh, Hunt!" he said in his magisterial way, "you're a month too late for the fair. Sit down, my good fellow. I have already put a round sum at his disposal, without any fuss, public or private."

This was a facer, but a worse one was to come.

"Did he take it?" Miss Chambre asked with seriousness; and Cobbett, as if he had been stung by a viper, recoiled.

Tears came smartly to his eyes, and he sat down without another word. Nor did he speak once more that night. "Oh, my dear, my dear, you are the angel on the threshing-floor!" says Rodono to himself.

The fact was that she, with perfect sincerity of vision, had detected an amiable failing of Mr. Cobbett's. Pantisocracy for him was foolishness. He was sure—he was sure all his life long—that any trouble of the lower orders could be salved with half-a-crown.

Here ended a painful episode in Miss Chambre's career. What she herself thought about it it is difficult to tell. She mentions it in a letter to Mary Fox. . . . "Rather a hateful party, very kindly meant. They make too much fuss—and it will all be put down to *him* . . . Mr. Cobbett. . . . I cannot say that he pleased me. He made me angry. . . . I believe I answered him sharply once. Mary, the notion! He offered Mr. V. money! And I must remember that our family brought that upon him with all the rest."

CHAPTER XVIII

B Y that same middle of June it is not surprising that
Miss Chambre was being talked about—talked about,
looked at, observed—but not as yet shunned. To reach
that stage of notoriety it would be necessary that she
should be sought elsewhere, by the public, for instance,
or by those who served the public. But this had not yet
happened, so that the polite world did little more than
stand tiptoe at a party to see "that Miss Chambre," or to
say that there seemed nothing in her—and consequently
nothing in "it."

Few credited the tale, or, at any rate, its more serious
involutions. At the worst it was an eccentricity due
to pedigree: "Colonel Chambre, my dear! and Lady
Hermione. . . . Lifted her himself over the railings,
and took her away pillion." Or, at best, it was politics:
"Lord Sandgate vows there was never any one like her.
She did it, he says, like an Empress-Queen." The answer to that was, "Or like the Duchess Georgiana," and
even that did her no harm. Politicians may go very far,
we know; but, politics apart, it did her position good;
for if you are driven to a preposterous parallel it shows
that you are at your wits' end for credit.

And then, as it were, on the heels of the visit to the Vernours, came that absurd supper in Piccadilly, which saved the girl's face. So it was Politics. The whole thing a Jacobin ruse from the beginning—"Politics, my dear! So I always supposed!"

In the clubs, it's true, tongues went more gaily. "Bet you she's kissed in a month," was taken; the book sent for, the entry made. "Colonel Despard bets Lord Miling ten to one in sovs. that Miss H. C. is—" etc. But there's a reason for that. In the clubs they read the newspapers—the *Examiner* to wit, to say nothing of the *Dwarf* and the *Gadfly* and *Peeping Tom.* The matter was too rich to have been missed by these scavenger-birds, and variations too fruitful. The Lady and the Butcher Boy: that came to be a popular cry, and made a score of ballads which might have floated the thing off into legend—so that in after years one would have read of Miss Chambre in company of Molly Legree and the Lass of Richmond Hill; and so they would, if they had been let alone to deal with it. It was the humourists who could really hurt, and who did their best, you may be sure. How they rang the changes! Broken hearts and bullocks' hearts, sheeps' heads and sheeps' eyes, cleavers and cleavings, again the Duchess's canvass with the lips: they had heavy hands in 1809; they spanked with the flat palm where we flick with the little finger.

And prints! I have before me a caricature where the

episode is lumped in your face. It's political, but it's
more—it's anacreontic. A fine young lady, bountifully
enriched in form and hue, a very Hebe, in the tell-tale
gown of the period—hiding little, suggesting much—
stands with drooping head and hands clasped. She looks
like a Circassian in the market-place—exposed. Then,
before her, rampant, is a florid youth, frocked and
aproned proper. He sharpens his blade on the steel, his
starting eyes are fixed upon her, towards the region
of the heart. It's not a bad likeness—makes him resemble
the Prince as a young man, high-coloured, square-
shouldered and fleshy. From his mouth issues a stream
of air which, expanding as it ascends, enfolds a legend.
"Cob-it, my hearty," we read, "it's prime meat, this
year's lamb. Now, miss, how will you have it cut?" In
the background Mr. Cobbett, to be guessed by his broad
back and gaiters, cries, "Buy, buy, buy!" and exhibits
crowned carcases to the mob; while Captain Ranald, un-
mistakable in cocked hat, hacks with his regulation sword
at a fine hog labelled "Caryll-cured." To put the whole
beyond a doubt is the flagrant title subscribed, "The
Groom of the Ch——re, or Cleaving to the Cleaver."
This had a great vogue, and one can only hope the fair
victim never heard of it. And I don't know whether it
appeared before or after Mordaunt's anecdote got about.
Pink Mordaunt he is in all the Memoirs. They must
have been very near together.

What Mordaunt had to say was that towards the end of

June the girl was walking from Berkeley Square, where she had been visiting, with Lady Barwise, her aunt, and that he, Pink, was escort. The weather was lovely, with the planes of Lansdowne House in their fulness of green —a perfect summer afternoon following a wet morning. Round the corner of James Street came a horse at a canter, and upon the horse, well back upon him, the reins loose, sat a fine young man, bareheaded, in blue smock and apron. He pulled up short to let the ladies cross; but it had been raining and the road was muddy. A spatter covered Mr. Mordaunt's nankeens, a fleck or two showed upon Miss Chambre's muslin. "Damn the lout!" cries Pink, and immediately begs pardon. And as he looks his apologies, says he, he is struck by the expression of Miss Chambre's eyes—fixed and attentive, as if waiting, as if expecting an order; and he notices the parting of her lips—as if she paused, but did not breathe. She was blushing divinely, she looked splendid, he said—but she was looking at the horseman who had just muddied her dress.

And then, for his climax, delivered in his best tones, "I give you my word of honour that she bowed to him— bowed, sir, as you or I to the old king. And I'll be shot, Johnny Russell, if he didn't accept it. That's the word, sir: *he accepted it*, as the Prince might take it from a bargee. You might—" he puffed his cheeks out, and you could see why they called him Pink—"you might have knocked me down with a feather-brush—by Gad, you might!" This was a story which lost nothing in the telling, and ran waxing all over town.

It's a true story. That was the first encounter she had with the redoubtable Vernour after her escapade in Brook Street—and often enough she had wondered when it would come upon her. And when it came, the girl did stiffen, did blush, did watch and wait, did bow her head— and was accepted. She was never asked to justify such proceedings, and had no one to whom to whisper of them —nor was she of the sort which lightly confides secrets to bosom friends; but she would have been perfectly simple about it. He was before her again—she knew him— she bowed. What else? That she was glad to see him? She was glad. That she had been waiting for it to occur, by accident? It must be by accident—that's of course. She might have so contrived as to meet him twice a day at the gates of Caryll House; his hours were known to the minute. But that could not be. That was for the Mrs. Moths, may we say, the Harriet Moons. But if she thought—and she had thought—she must have known that she would meet him casually, must have speculated on what she would do; and, being what she was, she would not have faltered. Without pretending to read her heart better than you can, that's how I put it before you. That's my idea.

As for Vernour, it is true that he bent his head to her when he received her greeting, that he looked at her seriously, that he raised his hand, but not to touch his forelock. It all depends on how that was done—whether lightly or with the deference usual from an inferior. Pink Mordaunt said that he jerked it up like a field officer acknowledging a sergeant's salute; but that may have been one of his after-touches. He was famous for his technique in these matters.

He added, certainly, details of what followed upon the encounter—sort of *mémoires pour servir* for a sequel. Her great colour, he said, endured up Hay Hill and across Piccadilly; somewhere past Arlington Street her composure came back, and she could give him sally for sally. He had, of course, sprung his rattle at the first glimpse of danger, and kept it going for most of the walk. He was true to the traditions of his caste, you see; and I hope she was grateful to him. She ought to have been.

Whatever Lady Barwise may have seen at the moment, she never turned a hair. But she thought proper to speak to her mother. "Mamma, you ought to stop this at once. It is certain to be talked about as it is, and heaven knows what it may lead to. Surely we have had enough of the man's horse! I do think that we might leave the newspapers to the Royal Family. I'm told that the Duchess of Suss——"

"I beg your pardon, Louisa," said her ladyship, "but I cannot think that my family can compete for scandal with the king's. I don't believe a word of your story. If she felt uncomfortable at meeting the man again, it's no wonder—and her own fault. She'll get over that.

The rest is pure imagination, if it's no worse. I must be allowed to remind you that you never got on with poor Hermione, and are hardly likely to esteem her children."

"Her children and Colonel Chambre's, mamma," said Lady Barwise.

"My grandchildren and your father's, my dear," the high old lady replied.

There was nothing more to be said, though the *impasse* was felt to be unworthy of Lady Morfa. And yet Lady Barwise had been justified if she had but known that, as a consequence of this walk, Hermia was sent off to Plashetts to the care of Lady Sarah Coigne, the baronet's mother. She was not sorry to go, and had pleaded for Harriet's companionship; but Lady Morfa had need of Moon, she said. So Moon remained in town, and solaced her brown eyes with tears, or whatever balm she could come by.

It was after ten days or so at Plashetts that there befell her another adventure of the kind. On this occasion she was alone in the great Morfa chariot, driving out to pick up her grandmamma, who had been breakfasting with Lord Sumnor. At the north end of Bond Street a horse had fallen under his yoke-fellow; there was a block; and in it, on his grey cob, sat Vernour.

He was close to her now, so close that their hands, stretched out, could have touched, so close that she could see the colour of his eyes when for one serious moment hers met them. This time, it's noteworthy, she did not bow, nor did he; but the greeting was the more intense for the muteness of it; behind the locked lips of each might be sensed a cry. His—"Oh, I see you there enthroned—and I kneel, I kneel. I am always on my knees!" And hers—"Here am I—what will you have of me?" And then another—"Turn away your eyes. I am afraid." It was she who avoided, for he did not. For how long she sat burning there is not to be guessed; all that can be said is that her grandmamma had no reason to complain of her vivacity when she joined her in the carriage. Another odd thing: when they were back at the house, and before Jacob Jacobs could lock the gates upon the divinities returned to the shrine, she had run out again, and had given Mother Cole a shilling.

Mother Cole was a weather-fretted old woman in a black bonnet and shawl, who swept the crossing in Cleveland Row. She was an institution as famous in her quarter of the town as Sir Jeffery Dunstan, Mayor of Garrat, in his. She was the familiar of princes and peers; it was said of her that Mr. Fox never delivered an important speech in the House without going over the heads of it with Mother Cole. She was a staunch Whig. Lord Rodono had presented Miss Chambre to this celebrity upon an early day, and much familiarity had ensued.

Matrimony was the sum of her discourse to ladies— matrimony with a wink for maternity: gallantry of that to gentlemen—with a wink for frailty. She rarely acknowledged Miss Chambre's greetings without a "When is it to be, miss?" and would shake her head at all laughing denials. On this occasion, whether it was the unwonted shilling, or a light not hitherto seen in the young lady's eyes, or a cheek too rosy, or a flutter in the voice, Mother Cole darted a penetrating glance, and said, "Ah, miss! ah, my pretty dear! 'Tis easy seen he's been by." Miss Chambre made no denials, but did not cease to blush. It was ridiculous, it may have been monstrous, but she was not offended.

CHAPTER XIX

PARLIAMENT was prorogued at the end of the month, three weeks after Lady Burdett's supper-party to the new heroine of Democracy. Gentlemen of the House of Commons were dismissed to their counties, admonished by a speech from the Throne to carry with them "a disposition to inculcate, both by instruction and example, a spirit of attachment to those established laws and that happy Constitution which it has ever been his Majesty's anxious wish to support," and which his Majesty's Ministers, it was to be understood, did chiefly enable him to support. Of such friends of ours as had counties to which they could repair, Lord Sandgate went into Wilts and Sir Francis no further than Wimbledon. Mr. Ranald returned to sea and the harrying of poor Lord Gambier; Lord Rodono, staying in town, broke his promise when he asked Miss Chambre to marry him, but it had not suited Lady Morfa to leave London so early, nor the Earl, her son, to repair to any of his counties. He was now at Brighton with the Prince and Lord Moira, and chose to keep Caryll House open for his occasional visits —to a cock-fight, or a dog-fight, to his tailor's, or to a certain villa in Brompton, where he was known as Captain Graham, and where there was also a Mrs. Graham, who lived chiefly in a pink silk wrapper. Later on in the summer, her ladyship intended for Bath and a round of visits before settling down for the autumn at Wrensham Park, in Leicestershire. Meantime, there remained a party or two, of a late blossoming sort, to be gathered— to which she went and took her grandchild; at one of which Tom Rodono slipped away from grace.

Meeting his mistress here, he fell to railing at the Piccadilly *fiasco*, for which he said somebody ought to have called Sandgate out. She was disposed to defend it, not finding it in her heart to scorn honesty even when it was compounded with shrieking vulgarity; but he was too sore to allow any justification. He remembered that Sandgate professed to worship what he had trailed in the miry clay.

"The thing was execrable," he said, "or no! it would have been execrable if it had not been so ridiculous—as it was, it was merely squalid. . . . I don't fancy that you cared for my cutting in. Bless you, I know that it was flattery in its way, and meant to be flattering— but there was too much of it. You can't eat butter out of spoons. I spoke my little piece because I thought you would have felt bound to say something, and wanted to spare you the necessity of dropping to orator Hunt's level, or old Cobbett's. The way it came to me is due to God."

"A jealous God," she said. He took that.

"Yes—that's truer than you think for. And I made you angry, I fancy—but I don't care. It would need more than your anger to keep me from defending you. You shall never be cheapened if I can help it. Orator Hunt—O Lord!"

She had not liked Mr. Hunt, so said nothing.

"Those fellows," he ran grumbling on, "ain't democrats, you know. You must be a gentleman to be a democrat—and a fine gentleman, too."

"Or a man," said she here, clinging to Tom Paine; but Tom Rodono wouldn't have it.

"No; a gentleman. In a matter of give and take— which is all this world, if it's to be habitable—you must be able for either. A man can take, but 'tis a gentleman who can give. Democracy without giving is flat impossible. Lafayette was a giver, so was your Eddy Fitzgerald—so's Bob Ranald, and so are you, in the making. So's Burdett, I don't doubt for a moment. But Sandgate! Sandgate's as much of a democrat as Bonaparte. . . . There are the old stagers now, whom it might have entertained you to meet—old classics, veterans. Tooke now, Parson Tooke! a hoary old spider, spinning philosophies, and then, with a microscopic eye, watching us try to live 'em out. Our disasters are his gain—they teach him a deal. They prosecuted him in '94, and might as well have burned St. Paul in effigy. Then there's the Major. God bless the Major! he's more hon-

est than Cobbett, because he has fewer half crowns
spend."

He reflected humorously, and chuckled at his thoughts.
"I'll tell you what, though: you've made an enemy of
William. You flicked him on a raw—for, of course, the
fact is that Vernour refused his crown-piece. The old
bull-frog would never have said a word of it if he hadn't
meant to quench the orator. That had to be done, and
then you had him. Oh, I love you for it! The neatest
turn of the wrist, and you spitted him like a master of
fence."

She told him she had never meant so much. "He
had been very kind to me—I was prepared to esteem
him highly. But—oh, he was dreadfully wrong—to
offer money to and then to talk about it. Horrible!"

"Bad enough for the Duke of York," said Rodono;
and then he made his proposal—in the same candid,
carefully moderate vein. "Your grandmamma won't
hear of me—but if you will, I can bear that. I've
enough for two. Don't ask me what I feel for you;
you'd waste your time—you can see right through me,
I know. And don't ask me what I have to boast of
—what pretences to make: they're mighty few. I've
done nothing so far. I threw up my commission for
the sake of Parliament, to please the parent chiefly.
There was our rotten borough, you know—rotting.
We'd always been in the House, he told me; and I be-

e him. We are of the sort that, somehow, always *is*
..ere. At the very outset, I sickened of it. '*Who will
show us any good?*' You talk of Pitt and Dundas—
but do you think Sam Whitbread's any better? Do you
think little Creevy's a patriot? Did Wardle hamstring
the Duke for the salvation of the country? However,
I'm not talking politics; you can make a man of me if
you choose. I'm in love with you, Miss Hermia, and I
want to get you out of this quagmire. You've a face like
a flower and a soul like a spirit of the fire. Give me my
way, and you shall bloom for ever in a clean air; and
your flame shall be fed with ambergris and frankincense.
Scotch! What do you say?"

There was but one thing to be said, and she said it,
though she disliked the giving of pain. She thought
him a lively and agreeable companion, and entirely to be
trusted; but she had a shrewd perception of the self-
esteem underlying his light-hearted words, and the life he
proposed to her was not promising. To make a man of
him if she chose? How could she help recalling him who
had assured her with such intensity of truth that
she had restored manhood to him also? Ah, there
had been no mock depreciation of himself in that
short-spoken man! And what else did Tom Rodono
propose? He was to be minister to an altar, on
which she sat and burned. No, no—with Tom for ever
extenuating his ministry, she could not burn; she would
"go out." The ministering must be the other way if

she were to live; and the mere thought of that made to heart leap—and in that leap poor Rodono was droppe.

She dismissed him with an assurance of friendship, which he was thankful to take, and an offered hand which he gallantly kissed. He met her on a later day as if nothing out of the common had occurred—which, as far as that goes, it had not; and she was grateful to him for that, because, to her, something singular *had* occurred. The Violet Intrigue had begun.

On that very morning, indeed, she received the first of a series of gifts—remarkable for its nature, persistence and mystery of origin—or, as a fact, she received three of them together, for they had begun to arrive two days before. Let me be precise in so singular a matter. Tom Rodono offered her the altar-seat on June 24th. It was on June 22d that the Violet Intrigue began.

A bunch of white violets, a good-sized bunch fresh-and-fresh, was left at Caryll House on the morning of the 22d at half-past eight in the forenoon. It was left at the porter's lodge by an elderly woman in a plaid shawl and black bonnet, with the simple message that it was for Miss Chambre, and "particular." The violets, smelling of wet hedgerows, were tied together with gardener's bast, and as the gate-porter said, when he was interrogated, "took him back—ah, and back and back they took him, they did!" He assured Miss Hermia that he had carried them into the house immediately and given them to one of the maids with the message as delivered to him, that "they was for Miss Chambre, and particular." He would swear that upon the Book, "before the Judges of Assize and their marshals, and the Grand Jury of Middlesex." To which of the maids? Ah, that was a puzzler; for he was getting on in years and took little stock of the maids. Twenty years, fifteen years back, had Miss Hermia asked him! Now he came to think of it, he did believe it had been to the black-eyed girl whom, on that account, they called Susan—though her name was Hester. He thought so, because he knew her father, who was a market-gardener at Mortlake. Yes, yes, and she had been sweeping the passage at the time; and he had said—his very words—"My dear, give this here to Mrs. Moth with my compliments, and say it's for Miss Chambre, and *very* particular." "Very" had been his addition, because "you know what gels are, miss." That was all he knew, except that violets had been brought to the door at the same hour ever since that morning.

Susan, the black-eyed, owned to having received the violets from Mr. Jacobs. She swore that she had put them on the tray with Miss Chambre's tea, toast, and letters, which Mrs. Moth was to take up. Three mornings, including this very morning, she had done the same thing. No; she owned that she had forgotten the message, that they were particular, or very particular. She was very sorry indeed, and shed tears.

It was now definitely thrust upon Mrs. Moth, who

evaded with practised ease. How could she have known
—she put that to Miss Chambre—that the violets were
particular? The first time she saw them she had thought
they got there by accident, that one of the maids had
dropped them out of her bosom, "or so," when preparing
the tea-tray—"for they receive such things, Miss Chambre, from their friends, as you know! And they put
them—well, where else can they put them, poor creatures?" Fine, scornful Mrs. Moth. On the second
morning, she owned she had had her doubts, and had
made inquiries. No—she had not inquired of Susan, but
in the housekeeper's room, of Mr. Progers, the butler,
and of Mr. Venning, the head footman, and of the first
housemaid; she confessed that she did not "have dealings" with the lower servants. The third morning she
had been positive that something was intended—"more,
I should say, miss, than meets the eye, as they say;" and
so she had brought all three bunches up together.

The thing was certainly odd, rather romantic in its
way. Who was this old woman? Let Jacob Jacobs of
the gates inquire. Meantime, the recipient met Lord
Rodono after his repulse with a new tenderness, feeling
pretty sure that the tribute was his. How extraordinary
was man! Ashamed of himself for the very thing which
could be his least reproach! Why, this sort of offering,
so contemned by your Moths, was exactly aimed at her
weakness. Simple, sincere, affectionate, humble things—
white violets fresh gathered—left at the gate by an old

woman—for Miss Chambre, and particular! She was honestly touched, and felt more kindness for Tom Rodono than she could have thought possible. She went out of her way to be kind to the violet-bringer. She wore the latest bunch at her breast, and looked down at it nestling there more than once or twice. Tom also looked, more than once or twice. She wore no other flowers or ornament, and he remarked upon it—and destroyed himself. "*Simplex munditiis*, eh? I approve," he said. She smiled upon him, very gently.

"I hoped that you would. They were a present to me this morning. An old lady's."

"Oho," said he, "you mustn't tell me that."

"Why, what else can I tell you? Honestly, an old lady brought them."

"Let's hope she's honest. I scent a broker."

She blushed. "Lord Rodono, you are not angry with me?"

"God forbid!"

"You should not be. I count you my friend—you and Grizel, of my best friends. I may prove you yet."

"Prove, prove. I ask nothing better."

"Well, find out who gives me violets every day."

"Every day! Is it so? Certainly, I'll do my best—but remember, I assassinate him if I find him." She went happily away with the thought that she had a romantic worshipper somewhere hidden, and that it was assuredly not Tom Rodono.

Jacobs, of the gate, could find out little or nothing from his old lady, who, frightened by his manner, or his gold-laced hat, or gold garter, took refuge in that sure harbour of old ladies, tears. Securely swimming in these familiar waters, she snuffled at ease. She said that she was a poor widow, by name Mrs. Matthews, Mrs. Matthews of the Highgate Road, glad to earn her pittance a week by honest courses. The money was paid her in advance for what she had to do—which was to go to such and such a street corner, receive a bunch of white violets, and take it to Caryll House gate. She did not know the person who gave them to her, and must not say what she knew of—him? As the Lord would have mercy upon sinners, she had not said *him* or *her;* she had said *person,* and "person" it must for ever be if she was to earn her money—which was material— and bread at thirteenpence-halfpenny the quartern. God pity the poor! She told Mr. Jacobs that any further questioning might lose it her; and with that she went away. Next morning, to her visible consternation, she had to hand over her violets to Miss Chambre herself.

That lady's custom was to ride every summer morning between half-past seven and nine; but to-day she had changed her mind, and returned punctually at the half-hour. She then saw the plaid shawl at the gates, and Jacob Jacobs, stately and remote, pretending that he had no notion what it was doing there. He waved his hand, and was about to explain the phenomenon to Miss

Hermia, who, in her fawn-coloured habit, open at the throat, in her great hat and grey veil, high on her shining horse, looked like a queen of Amazons, able to ride underfoot without ruth a whole phalanx of poor widows from the Highgate Road. The little peering face shrank into the black bonnet, the plaid shawl shivered; its poor tenant was making for the water again—that sure harbour of tears. "Oh, miss—oh, my lady, I should say, whatever will become of poor me?"

"Nothing but good, I am sure," said Miss Chambre. "Are those my violets? Thank you very much." She took them, stooping from her saddle; carried them to her mouth, and snuffed long at them. "They are as fresh as the day. I never had such a present before. It is most kind of you. I am most grateful."

"Bless you, my lady! 'Tis not me that gives them to your ladyship."

"I suppose not. Why should you? But will you please to thank the giver for me? It is a very kind thought."

"Yes, miss, yes, my lady, I will. And proud enough— Lord have mercy! what was I saying?"

"Don't be afraid—don't say more than you wish to say. Good-bye." She struck through the gates, followed by the groom—then pulled up short. "Stay a moment," she called to the dazzled creature, and turned the horse. "Will you let me—give you something? Will you? For your trouble and kindness, I mean." Horror blenched the peering eyes.

"Oh, no, my lady, I dursn't! I'm forbidden—it 'ud be the end of me—of my pittance a week. Oh, pray, pray!"

Miss Chambre coloured. "I beg your pardon. I ought to have known better. Perhaps we shall meet again. I hope so." She turned and rode to the door; she went upstairs, her violets to her mouth; wore them that night, and, in fact, got into the habit of using no other adornment whatsoever. It would be hard to say why the gift pleased her so much—whether it touched some secret spring of romance, or appealed to her passion for simplicity; but there is no doubt that she came to count upon white violets for her bosom or hair every evening. The unknown lover had chosen a powerful advocate; but he remained unknown.

In July, when the Earl of Morfa went to Ireland on private business of his Prince's, Lady Morfa was to travel in semi-state to Bath, Hermia and the brown-eyed Moon with her. The latter had hopes of the west, which she admitted to nobody, but Hermia, who concealed nothing, plainly said that she should miss her violets terribly —an admission which made Miss Moon look arch. She had seen trembling Mrs. Matthews but a few days before, and told her as much. "Good-bye, Mrs. Matthews; I'm going to Bath with my grandmother. I can't hope to see you there, I'm afraid."

"No, indeed, miss, you cannot. But let's hope for happy returns."

"Let us hope for all sorts of things. I haven't heard from Portugal, from my brother, for a month. He's a wicked boy not to spare me a letter. And that's what I hope for most in the world. Good-bye, Mrs. Matthews." And then the chariot bore her away. Among the farewells she did not make was one to Mrs. Vernour, of Brook Street. She had been afraid of meeting Vernour there.

Bath proved to be very full; the King's Parade crowded on the fine, cool mornings; the Pump Room like Almack's. One of the first people she met with when she walked abroad was Sir George Coigne, in snuff-brown coat, white breeches, and the neatest pair of boots you ever saw. Harriet Moon betrayed herself by a fierce pressure of the arm. "Oh, Hermy, look, look!"

"Where then, my dear? Oh, I see. It's George Coigne," and then she returned the pressure.

Sir George was all affability. Upon his honour, a singular thing! Quite a happy meeting—no place like Bath for happy meetings, was there now? He hoped Miss Moon was very well; he was charmed to meet Miss Moon—and Cousin Hermy, looking positively radiant. He must positively pay his respects to Aunt Morfa that day. It was pleasant to listen to such enthusiastic babble; no place like Bath indeed.

Miss Hermia was undoubtedly radiant—with her own

small triumph to sun herself in. Moth had come to her that morning all of a twitter—bursting with confidences, noddings and bridlings. "Guess, if you please, miss, what I have brought you! Only to think of the devotion of some gentlemen!"

"My violets?" said sleepy Hermia. "Give them to me." And into her bed they went.

CHAPTER XX

FROM Bath to Bowood, from Bowood to Bramshaw Demesne, where my Lord Sandgate acted the respectful lover, and Sir George, whose part was double, had his work cut out for him; from Bramshaw to Wrensham—the Morfa place in Leicestershire—I do not propose to follow Miss Chambre so faithfully as did her daily bunch of violets. I believe that they missed her for some six days out of six weeks, and most of those were days spent on the road. One must suppose that somebody of the household was in the secret—the bridling Mrs. Moth, for instance, perhaps even a grateful Moon—if one is to account for the fact that an order for flowers, emanating from London, could be obeyed to within a few days in Somerset, in Wilts, and in the Midlands. How else but by private intelligence could the tribute-bringer understand that Lady Morfa would anticipate her visit to Bramshaw by three days and have cut Bowood short by three—just because she did not like the butter there? Nobody of Miss Chambre's exclusive acquaintance could have known of such a vagary; and yet Moth professed the blankest ignorance! Miss Moon, strangely enough, was not asked; and Miss Moon was very intelligent.

Perhaps there was a fear that she might at once dispel so absorbing a mystery—I don't know. At any rate, the beleaguering lover, whoever he was, had hit upon siege tactics which the great Marlborough could not have bettered. But his master-stroke was delivered at Wrensham Park, where, in the heavy heats of August, there came sorrow upon the lady whom he served. On the 22d of that month the newsboy brought Sir Arthur Wellesley's despatch, which London had had on the 20th. We read in that how the allies had beaten Victor at Talavera and driven him over the Alberche; a signal triumph for our arms. But the death-roll was heavy in officers and men, and held the name of Ensign Richard Caryll Chambre, "a promising officer." A *parterre* of violets would recoil before such a blow as that.

The house was full of people at the time. The family was in force—Barwises, young and old, including Lord Barwise himself, on his yearly duty by his wife's side; Lord John Botetort, Lady Carinthia Gell-Gell and her flock of Gell-Gells, with those high noses of theirs, which made them so like geese on a common; Sir George Coigne and his brother Adolphus, a callow youth with a voice on probation; the Lukyns, on their way to Hawick, Mr. Mordaunt on his to Welbeck—Pownalls, Considines, Trembletts, and a half-score names more. It was passably gay, sketching parties, archery and riding parties, dancing till the small hours and what-not. Of our intimates, Miss Chambre was certainly the happiest of the

happy, for her fund of common-sense gave her the power
of being happy when she chose; and I think that Miss
Moon was the most interested. Sir George had brought
himself into such a state of love-twitters that his fine legs
knocked together at the knees whensoever he found himself alone with the lady of his worship. Miss Moon, very
much aware of it, made it her business to see that he
twittered just enough to twitter anon—but no more.
And he must never twitter so much that it should be perceptible to anybody else—save, perhaps, Hermia. She,
her feelings obviously engaged, could be trusted; and besides, Miss Moon, I am sorry to say, having found out
that she could trust her friend to the uttermost, had begun to despise her somewhat.

The blow fell first upon her ladyship, who certainly
quailed before it. By custom, the postbag was put into
her hands by the house-steward, opened in her presence
by Harriet Moon, and its contents distributed by herself; and on that day fate had brought, side by side with
its fatalest, a belated letter from the boy himself de-
scribing the passage of the Douro—"rare fun, my
dear," he had written, "I swam it!" Lady Morfa, who
had put that letter apart, to be handed over in due course
to its owner, suddenly stopped Harriet as she was tip-
toeing away to deliver it. "Stop," she had called out in
a curious, dry voice; and Harriet, looking round, saw
her shaking over the *Morning Post*. "Bring that back
to me." Which Harriet did, quaking. Lady Morfa

took it, but could not hold it still. "I'll give her that myself—presently," she said. "Get me my smelling-salts, my dear. I want 'em." She had never called Moon "her dear" before. Something had happened.

The salts revived her. "Thankye, I'm better," she said—and then, impatiently, "Put all those away—I can't see to 'em now. I've something to do. Where's Miss Chambre?"

"She is riding, my lady, with Miss Honoria and Mr. Mordaunt."

"Ah!" That was something like a sob in the harsh old voice. "Well, leave me alone for the present. When Miss Chambre returns, let her come to me. Stay, though —I'll go through those letters first." And so she did, like the stark old Norman that she was.

She took the best, the only possible line with the girl; nobody can deny it her. "Come to me, my child," she had said, having complete mastery now of her voice and nerve; and when Hermia came near and put her hand on her shoulder, she went on, "Sit down. I want to talk to you as reasonably as may be." Hermia sat on a stool by her knees, and Lady Morfa, not trusting her hands, hid them in her folded arms and addressed herself. . . .

She was heard to the end—without a catch of the breath or stir of a finger to stop her; and at the close, after a moment of silence, Hermia said, "May I have my letter, please?" It was put into her hands, she broke seal, she read it through. Such was her tension at the time that I believe she could have read it aloud. Watched by her grandmamma, she sat on looking at the sweet-bitter sheets, and then she said gently, "My dear love! How he loved it all!"

Then something snapped: "Oh, granny, granny, what shall I do now?"—and she gave way—her face in the old woman's knees. The rest is sacred—too sacred for me, at least. Lady Morfa, within a year after it, had cause to remember the child who could see her heart's joy shiver, and yet hold up her head. . . .

They got the house emptied of all but the most intimate. Sir George, very much the gentleman, was one of the first to go. "No place for us, my boy," he said to his brother Adolphus; "we'll make ourselves scarce." He kissed the hand of his aunt, the fingers of his Harriet, and steered his coach for Wendover, Plashetts, and partridges. He took Lord John with him as far as Northampton, whence that nobleman made his way to Newmarket. Lady Carinthia repaired to town in order to speed Mr. Gell-Gell towards Baden-Baden; only Lady Barwise remained, she and her immovable Barwises; and Archdeacon Caryll—the Honourable the Venerable, as Lady Morfa (fine old Erastian!) always had him addressed—joined the party for consolatory purposes. He was famous for his extempory prayers.

Tom Rodono, who was in town, had written her a short letter, dated the 20th, which arrived a day or two later than the news. "If I am truly your friend, I must be thinking of you now; and if you are truly mine, you will know that," he had begun; and then, with a good deal of adroitness, he had praised the dead Richard for being all Chambre and no Caryll—whereas the truth was exactly the other way. Not a scrap of him was Chambre. What would he have said, pray, of his sister's summer exploits? Of the supper at Sir Francis's, the Phrygian cap on a Caryll head, of a Cobbett's lips brushing a Caryll cheek? And of other still more dangerous descents, what would he have said? She had gone her way with the fire of a Chambre blown by a Caryll pride, and if the truth is to be told, never once in her late crusade had she stayed to consider what Dick would have thought of her doings. Nor did she think now, as she fought with her sorrow, or lay prone on her face and let it do its worst. But she replied to Rodono's letter with a gratitude which showed itself plainly. "It is certain that you have a friendship for me, or you could not have said so many things to please me. I try to be like Dick, and to bear his death as he would have borne mine. We loved each other dearly, but I hope that need not stop for such a thing as earthly loss. Give Grizel my best love when you see her. I shall hear from her soon, I know. Your obliged and grateful HERMIA MARY." In a postscript: "Grandmamma is all that is kind. I don't think I ever understood her before. Her, and Grizel, and you—I have many friends."

Rodono's letter had come on or about the 24th, and on

that day also the violets ceased to come. She had not noticed, naturally, that they had been continued for the first two days of her mourning—but she noticed their cessation after a time, and was touched by it. The giver of them, certainly, lost nothing in her regard. On the contrary, that was the first of his fine strokes.

Her recovery was slow, but need not detain me; nothing of moment to the tale occurred until she returned to town. Lady Morfa kept her at Wrensham through September, a true act of sacrifice on her own part, since she panted to be in London, in the thick of events. Mr. Canning and Lord Castlereagh must quarrel—did quarrel; must meet—did meet; Lord Castlereagh was shot in the thigh; both Ministers resigned: and she not there to give and exchange nods and winks! I hope that this may be imputed to her for righteousness, for it was righteous.

In October, still in pursuit of rational distraction for her girl, she posted further north. Morfa Mawr, the great castle in Flintshire, was opened, and discreetly filled with "family" and close friends. The unavoidable Barwises came, of course; the Archdeacon carried his dyspepsia, his prayers, and his rhubarb lozenges on with him; the Charles Botetorts were added; and the head of their house, Lord Badlesmere—Marquis of Badlesmere, no less—stayed for a week. Lady Grizel was made welcome, and Lord Rodono, considered perfectly safe, was allowed to shoot pheasants. As for Harriet Moon, she was packed off to her mother at Ludlow for her holidays.

But in November Whig nature could no longer refrain itself, but wailed so loudly in Lady Morfa's breast that it could not be denied. The Duke of Portland was dead, and the Lord only knew what that might involve. The Prince of Wales had hurried to town; Lords Grey and Grenville sat in their houses of call, asking to be asked out. Mr. Sheridan was exceedingly busy; all the Whig captains had flocked to their standards; the Radicals, with Lord Sandgate to deploy them, hovered on the outskirts of either camp. Plot and counterplot were thickening the air, and Lady Morfa failed to conceive how strategy could be upheld unless she were there to nod and wink. She had heard, also, for certain, that another Duke—he of Devonshire—was infallibly to be married: a Whig—a duke—a Cavendish to be married, and no Caryll to be there? Forbid that, heaven! The great chariot took to the road; the weeping skies proclaimed its wisdom. Rural England, dissolving into grey mist, passed by them like a dream, and with the dream went sorrow, and on its heels hope was born again. The lamps, the bustle, the cobbles, and the cries of London proclaimed to our Miss Hermia that she could still live, that she could stand alone—ah, and look for happiness yet to come. Dick was in heaven, and she full young. Dick was in heaven, and she in thriving London and the press of this world's business. Her prayers had been said and her tears let fall. Dick was in heaven—hey, now, for London and Reform! She really did wonder whether the Whigs would come in.

Jacob Jacobs stood bowing at the gates; the canary-breeched giants lined the long vestibule. Brown-eyed Miss Harriet, very pretty, very smiling and deferential, came out to curtsey to her ladyship, to be enfolded and kissed by her champion. The dogs came wriggling and wagging about her skirts: great fires, brave lights, closed curtains, a tea-table—a pile of letters—hey, indeed, for London and Reform! The girl stood for a moment and absorbed all this cheer and substantial comfort. She filled her bosom with its warmth and opened her heart to its allure, what time from their huge gilt frames stately gentlemen and satin-gowned ladies—Vandyckish, Lely-ish, Knellerian, Reynoldsian—looked benignly down upon another Caryll beauty. Yes, yes, life was good—and Dick in heaven. Life for ever—and love—and Reform!

After tea, Harriet Moon took her upstairs, and when they were in the corridor, half way down it, stopped her unexpectedly, put her arm round her and kissed her close.

"You happy dear! you beautiful, happy dear," she said.

"Foolish child! you'll squeeze me to death."

Harriet kissed her again. "Darling, I must tell you something—prepare you for something. A secret! Your violets came again this morning."

Hermia felt that she betrayed herself in more ways than one. Harriet soon found out how her heart was beating. "Yes, indeed. They came this morning—by Mrs. Matthews. Oh, don't you wonder who it can possibly——?"

"I don't know," says Hermia. "I shall be glad to see them. They welcome me." Harriet renewed her kissings; and that night Hermia wore her violets in her black gown. It may be admitted that she had cried over them, and held them to her lips.

The Master-stroke had been dealt.

CHAPTER XXI

WHICH CONTAINS A CURIOUS CONFESSION

WHEN the Marquis of Edlogan married a perfectly insignificant and unconsidered Miss Augusta Poyning, of Huntingdonshire, with a fortune of no more than five thousand pounds; and when Lord Sandgate urgently renewed his suit for Miss Chambre's hand, Lady Morfa knew very well that she must bring Sir George Coigne to the point. It was the more pressing because her ground of definitely declining that noble person had been that George Coigne was already brought there. If such a sacrifice to the gods of battle could be predicated of her ladyship for one moment, it might almost appear that she had burned her boats—or her granddaughter's boats.

But she had not so considered the matter when, in her most urbane, constitutional, '89 manner, one fine hand upon my lord's sleeve, she had taken him into her confidence after this fashion. "My dear lord," she had said, "I am sure I can trust you with a little secret—secret for secret, is it not?—and, therefore, don't hesitate to tell you that my hope of some years' standing is about to be realised. You will be the last to misunderstand my satisfaction in a family match. It can only be known to a man of property and position how many difficulties are to be solved in that way—and in no other, so far as I can see. My nephew, George Coigne, is to have Hermia Mary—we hope this season. There is really no reason why he should not have his way in that. It is so happily arranged, nothing could be better. She will have my Botetort property when I die—it would have been her brother's had not Providence seen fit to dispose of the poor lad; as you know, it joins the Coigne place. I believe—Propert gives me to understand—it will near double the rental. It will more than double the acreage; and a great point with George Coigne is that the shooting will be greatly improved. It will be a different thing altogether, he tells me. So everybody will be pleased, and Hermia, I think you'll allow, is a very fortunate girl. I make no excuse for wearying you with these domestic concerns; you have been kindness itself, and I am sure I need not repeat that nothing, literally nothing but family interests, family duty, could withhold me from an alliance so gratifying to my family, and so acceptable to the child, as that which you have done me the honour to propose." So there was an end of Lord Viscount Sandgate.

In saying so much as this, in revealing her settled purpose before it had become anything more, she had no reason in the world for supposing that it would not be carried out to the letter. There did not exist in the Caryll-Botetort annals any instance, known to her, where the pleasure of the reigning Caryll or Botetort was not punctually and cheerfully performed. Lady Hermione, to be sure, always crops up to break the sequence—but that was an elopement, and she had brought her into the fold again when the Colonel was removed. And Lord Sandgate, to whom such a state of mind was very familiar, accepted his repulse like the fine gentleman he was, wished the young couple every·happiness, begged his respectful duty to Miss Chambre, kissed hands and bowed himself out. He was sincerely in love, and would not own himself beaten yet. "She and I together," he thought, "might lead England a stage nearer. But no! It's pheasants for ever—eh? Oh, George Coigne!"

Meeting Lord Rodono at Brooks's, I fear that he broke a confidence which he could not regard as seriously one; and that he could not, shows how seriously he regarded his own.

"I'm a beaten man, Tom," he said. "I'm winged, sir. Mother Morfa's refused me."

"What! that old game-bird?" says Rodono, who sometimes played the fool. "I never suspected you in that preserve. Why, she's five-and-seventy."

"She has the wiles of Circe about her, whatever. Let me tell you that she's made me feel pretty swinish. George Coigne's the man—George Coigne! She's marrying the loveliest girl in England—the warmest-hearted, the boldest—to a cock-pheasant, by God!"

Rodono shook his head, knowing better. "No, no,

you're out there. George Coigne'll never get her. She won't look at him."

"The old dragon's settled it, she tells me. The properties march, it seems. And there's the shooting—Oh, heaven, shooting—and Hermia Chambre!"

Lord Rodono could not approve of his acquaintance's methods, but did not find it possible to deny that, after his manner, he was serious. And if Sandgate chose to unbosom himself, ought not he? So he said, "You are a suitor, are you? I hadn't known that; and perhaps I ought to tell you that I am also."

"I supposed it," said Sandgate; "indeed, I may say that I knew it. Well, I wish you the joy denied to me."

Tom was touched. "That's very good of you, Sandgate—but I've been dismissed, by the goddess's self." Lord Sandgate raised his head.

"Did you——?"

"But I did. I swore that I would not—but I did it. Oh, she was kindness itself—has a liking for me, I'll swear to that. But it's love, sir, it's love that will open her wings—mark me, nothing else! And when they're open—she'll soar—she'll tower! It's not that she's cold, insensible, a Marcella for Cervantes's shepherd; she's not been touched, she's folded, has never felt the sun. And, for me, I'm not the god. Oh, she's rare!"

"She's divine—could set England free!"

Rodono threw himself deeper into his chair. "England!—oh, your divided duty. You're but half a lover,

Sandgate—and that won't do. Now I own myself want-
ing in the godlike; but, at least, I'm a neck-or-nothing
man, and don't give a curse for England."

"Why should you, Scotchman? But you'll try again?"

"I shall, indeed."

"Well, I await you. Then, by your leave, I'll break
a lance."

"With her?"

"With no other."

"You are very amiable. I feel that we ought to shake
hands upon it."

"We'll take it as done, Tom. When will you——?"

"To-night. At D—— House. Do you go?"

"No, indeed. I leave you the field."

Lord Rodono made his essay, with results which set him
blinking his eyes. It was done in the library of D——
House, late at night. She heard him with gently bent
head and gently lowered eyes; heard him out—and then,
with a lovely, tender, friendly look which cut him deeply,
quickly rose, took his arm, and, as they went out together, leaned her head almost to touch his shoulder.
"Dear friend," she said, feeling that she knew him by
heart, "you are so good to me—but don't tease me just
now. You force me to say what I should not—you make
me feel it your due. I am not quite free—now."

"Oh! Then I must behave myself. I did not guess
that."

"No, no. Nor did I—until lately; but now I think that I am sure." He was puzzled; had thought that he knew all her intimates. She saw him frowning over the problem, and stopped him by the door.

"You should know at once if—it's very extraordinary —if I knew myself. But——"

Now he stared. "What are you saying to me?"

"I am telling you the literal truth—that I am not sure."

"Of yourself?"

"No, no. Of the person."

"The *person!*" Lady Morfa's generic term!

"Well, I suppose that there must be a person——" and as he gazed blankly at her, she looked down at the white knot in her bosom. "There's my lover," she said, "and there's my heart. Ask me no more—I am drifting, but I have confidence. I am very happy—and you may wish me joy. I believe that."

Psyche! Psyche, and the Unknown God!

After that, he had a grim interest in watching from afar Lord Viscount Sandgate run his career and break his lance against the violet shield. No bones were broken, but the politician was unhorsed. She liked him less, respected him more than his brother in opposition; she felt the honour of his regard, and told him so. "You make me very proud, Lord Sandgate," she had said; and he—"But you may make me the proudest man in England." When she shook her head, he knew that he was on his back. He never asked her again; but would always declare that he could not cease to love her. He did not discuss his failure with Rodono, nor did that gentleman impart to him any hint of the curious confidence he had himself received. Lord Rodono had never cared for Sandgate's way of involving love in political ambitions, and could never really forgive him for the supper-party in the Piccadilly house—to which, rightly or wrongly, he attributed all that was now fast approaching. He withdrew himself, therefore, from his colleague's society; and Sandgate, a very proud man, was not slow to perceive it and to make it exceedingly easy.

As to Miss Chambre's confession, that had been perfectly true. She had known, from the day she returned to London, that she was deeply engaged; and from the moment of surrender had not ceased to triumph in the completeness of it. With whom was she, then, in love? She couldn't tell. She ignorantly worshipped—but loyally, with unswerving faith and unfailing thankfulness. The veiled lover breathed—she knew that much; he lived and breathed—through violets. All that they signified, all that their coming, all that their ceasing to come, and coming again, as it were, on the surging of the flood—all that he was. Constant, curiously subtle, mysterious, reticent, delicate, modest yet direct; there she was sure of him; he could have been modelled after that pattern. He would be very strong—that's of course; strong not only to do, but to refrain from doing,

when doing would be flagrant. He would never tire,
never falter in his purpose, never change in his plan;
his delicacy would make him subtle, and his modesty
keep him on continual guard—and yet, she was sure of
this—when the time came, he would bluntly declare his
passion—there would be no "May I——? Dare I——?
Might I hope——?" but instead, "Girl, I love you;
come." And that was to be a lover indeed—and to such
a lover she was proud to yield. She declared to herself
that she would follow him all over the world, "in a white
petticoat," like the love-lorn lady of olden time. Tall or
short, dark or fair, noble or simple—these accidents
never troubled her at all. That he was gentleness itself
was certain. Could such a tribute ever have been paid
by a clown to a lady?

What of her earlier concern? What of the timid eyes
and flushing cheeks with which she had hitherto faced
the man whose cause she had espoused? She could afford
to smile to herself now when she remembered that Vernour
had been able to trouble her heart's ease; and, what's
more, she had been able to meet him frankly and pleas-
antly; to accost him in the court, to nod to him in the
street, and to admire him for what she understood him
to be rather than for what she had made of him out of
her own enthusiasm. To Captain Ranald, who had come
back from sea, she had often spoken of the young man;
she had been to see his mother, too, and spent an hour
very happily there, and then one day, not long before

she made her strange confession to Rodono, she had met Vernour himself face to face and talked with him as an equal.

She had been in the company of Lady Grizel Turnbull, on a duty walk in the Mall. There it was that she suddenly came upon Captain Ranald—with him David Vernour in a black suit. Everything had followed very simply. Ranald had bowed, had introduced "my friend, Mr. Vernour—Lady Grizel Turnbull"; then Vernour had made his bow, and Miss Chambre had offered him her hand. Ranald had plunged into rattling sea-talk with Lady Grizel, prodding the grass as if it had been Mr. Croker; Hermia, bold in company, had opened to Vernour.

"You make a holiday?" He regarded her seriously. "No—not that. I am on a committee with Mr. Ranald. But I have left business."

"Ah! and you leave London?"

"Yes. I am going into Wiltshire. Lord Sandgate has offered me a farm." Her thoughts were wide; presently she asked him a question.

"You heard of my brother's death?"

He bowed gravely. "Yes. I had heard. He died well —as he had lived."

"Yes, I believe it. Yet he was made to live."

"He did live," said Vernour simply. "His death was life—to him."

"That is well said. You were in London at the time?"

"I am always in London. Yes, I read it—and thought of you."

She had no answer ready for that. She asked him, Had he spoken at Westminster? He had, it seemed, and was to speak again soon. But politics just now seemed to her a foolishness.

She said, "Mr. Ranald doubts the value of speeches."

"So do I," he agreed, "but we make way by holding back the people back. We must win on those terms."

"Yes, yes, you must win." She looked at him, and then away. "You are strong."

"We get stronger every day—by holding back. You head up your waters—and one day——"

She laughed here, feeling the triumphant certainty. "Oh, that day!"

"It will be a day on which to live," he said. "May I be on the crest of the breaking wave!"

Once again she found courage to meet his intent regard, and to smile her sympathy. "You, too, love battle."

"I hate war," he told her; "but I love fighting—with my head."

"With your head?"

He paused, and she had to search for his answer. It came slowly. "My heart, if you will. That instructs my head." She looked at the ground.

CHAPTER XXII

IN the meantime, the bringing of Sir George Coigne to a point caused visible agony to that cheerful and prosperous gentleman of Bucks; caused beads of sweat to break out upon that candid front, and a perfectly normal heart to knock irregularly at a perfectly fitting waistcoat. The "going," as he put it, was so exceedingly nice: how not to offend his aunt, how not to lose his Harriet—how, above all, to adjust his theory of fine manners, which, according to him, lay absolutely in agreeing with every word addressed to you, with his assumption that if a man of thirty thousand a year could not choose his own wife, damn it all, who could?

But here was hard work for a good, easy man. " 'Pon my life, aunt, I'm very much gratified—highly gratified. There's nothing in life would please me more than to meet you in this. That property, Encombe, Morehays, and all that—oh, it marches with me all the way, I'll not deny. Fine property! Fine woods and plantations—wants thinning, though; I meant to have told your man about that, last time I was there. It's a very handsome offer, very handsome indeed, by Jove! And, as you know, I always liked Hermy—full of spirit, full of dash, alive up to the chin—eh? Oh, Lord, yes!" He was failing fast; could hardly see the brown eyes of his attraction—and upon Hermia's account he had positively no more to say.

Nor did her ladyship need him to say any more. "Very well, then, George, that's settled, I suppose?" was how she proposed to close the discussion.

"Eh? Settled?" He was shocked. "Well, you know, aunt, a man must have time, you know."

"It is usually the lady who asks for that," she said drily. But he leaped at it.

"That's what I meant, you know—exactly. Course she must! Very proper. And I'll tell you what I feel about it—that a man ought to *choose* his time. She'd shy off at once if I—if I rushed her at it, and all that. No, no; one goes tenderly at these things. I'm certain of that— dead certain it's the wise plan."

"It's not at all my wish to dictate to you, George— that you know. Let it be understood that you do speak to Hermia and I will see to my part of the arrangements." And then she saw fit to mention Lord Sandgate's renewed offer of the other day, and her own act of boat-burning. "So you see, George, you are, as it were, upon your honour!"

Sir George Coigne's eyes stared roundly in his head. Really, his aunt was a high lady—"put's a man on his honour as easy as I'd put one on his back. And Sand-

gate, poor devil! Bad luck, that—damned bad luck all
round! What I'd give my head to be out of, he'd give
his to be in with—and if that don't make this world out a
pretty queer kind of place, I'll be shot." Thus he mused
as he drove home in the dusk, and then fell to dreaming
of his slim Harriet, and to picture her peering haplessly
out of a window towards the North. "The sweetest,
gentlest creature! The kindest girl! Shall I play false
to a little heart like hers? Dare I turn my back on those
little kissed hands? By heaven and earth, if my honour's at stake, it's for her—and no other." Thus
greatly the baronet testified of his love.

I am one of those—one, I know, of a minority—who
think it possible that a lady's eyes can be too large; dif-
fering here from Mr. Romney and Monsieur Greuze. I
am sure that Harriet's were too large, beautiful as they
were, deep and velvety brown. But they loomed, positively, in her face, which was small and thin, and not remarkably well shaped: too broad in the brow, too sharp
in the chin, with cheek-bones prominent enough to earn
her the name of the Death's Head Moth among those
who were untouched by her peculiar charm. Eyes apart,
her mouth was very pretty: she had those features to
her credit, and her courteous, deprecating ways. She
was thin, with no figure to speak of, timid and low-voiced,
sparing in the use of her fine eyes. She was, however,
very intelligent.

Here is a proof of her intelligence: shortly after this re-

cent visit of Sir George's she had sought Hermia out,
and piece by piece had confided to her the whole story
of her entanglement with Lord Morfa, which, upon her
showing, did not, after all, amount to very much. There
had been interviews, certainly, and meetings—in the
Mall and elsewhere; there had been kisses—"Oh, what
must you think of me? Oh, Hermy, how can I tell
you these things!" But—and she laid stress upon this—
there had been *no* letters. The affair—she called it "attentions"—had begun soon after her taking duty with
her ladyship—a time when, she said, she had hardly
dared refuse Lord Morfa's gallantry, and would not
have known how to do so. Since his unexpected visit to
Petersham—he had kissed her then, when they were looking at the guinea-pigs—she had hardly seen anything
of him; had heard he was entangled elsewhere, felt nothing but esteem for him, as the son of her patroness, etc.
She was much more serious than she had been, and regretted that the cloister was forbidden by the English
Church. Questioned as to her other affair with Sir
George Coigne, she made it evident that it stood on a
different level. It had been very honourable on the gentleman's part: a first meeting at Wrensham, a twisted
ankle, a visit and a drive in a dog-cart at Plashetts, and
an interrupted avowal in town. No more than that, she
vowed.

This was the state of Miss Moon's affairs when Sir
George swore that he would be true to her.

The oath may have been supererogatory, and it may have been fine: in the latter case, it urgently required the test of deeds. Yes—but what deeds were open to a young man oppressed with a theory of manners? So far as he could see, there was but one thing to be done—make a clean breast of it to his cousin Hermy, and throw himself upon her generosity. He returned to London, therefore, and wrote to her requesting an interview in the Mall, if she could find it convenient to walk there on some fine morning, "suitably accompanied." He prided himself upon a phrase which was not only eminently proper, but might cause her to select for *duenna* his Moon. This Hermia would have done—for she was benevolent if her intelligence was not great in these matters—had not his Moon excused herself. She vowed that she could not possibly meet Sir George just yet—that she needed time to reflect—that he had not led her to suppose—and the usual half-phrases more. So Hermia went out with Mrs. Moth in waiting.

Sir George's agitation was such that he lost grip of his theory of manners. A hasty "Upon my soul, Hermy, this is more than common kind of you," was all he could manage before he plunged into the thick of his matter.

"Your grandmother's a wonderful old woman, you know—masterful! By the Lord, she's made things awkward for me—and for you, too, you know—oh, yes, you're in it, deep! and I'm quite aware that it's worse for you—don't flatter myself, eh? Oh, she's a rare one!

I remember very well poor old Uncle Morfa—fine man
he was in his prime, and when he was let alone—he needed
that, I must say—two-bottle man, regular as gun-fire—
I remember his saying to me once— Well, well, he's
gone to his rest, eh? And—well, Hermy, my dear, the
thing is, what are we to do—eh?"

"I have no notion," she admitted; "nor shall I ever
have, unless you begin at the beginning."

"I know, I know—that's the right thing," said the poor
baronet. "Nothing like candour in these things. Your
grandmother carries it too far, though. Candid! She
uses a club—she lays you down! Eh? Like a pipe of
port, by George! Why, she said to me of you—when
we were talking one day last season—Oh, Lord!—well,
never mind that. But—look here, Hermy, I'll ask
you right out, and have done with it. How's Miss
Moon?"

"So that's the beginning, is it? She's very well, I
think."

"Hermy, I adore that lady. I've been head and shoulders in it this two years; constant as—anything. I
could kneel at her feet, I do believe—it 'ud do me good,
good! And I'd do it—that I'm ready to swear to—anywhere, by heaven!"

"You wouldn't swear it to grandmamma," she said, and
sobered him.

"No," he said, "no, I wouldn't. That's just it. We've
got to the point at last. I wouldn't, you know. She's

extraordinary—she has a way of putting you on your honour—No! I'll be shot if I know how to do that. But I do think it's a queer state of— And look here, Hermy, you know—there's more in this than meets the eye."

"If it is ever to reach my eye, George," said she, "you must explain yourself."

Then, to her quiet amusement, he told her the tale—to her amusement, because her grandmother, she thought, might as well have commanded the sun to shine by night as that this round-faced, consternated baronet should marry her. Her grandmamma and her placid disposition! Why, when her fate was fixed—when in a few hours' time her violets—her lover—would be lying on her breast! She wore them always at night, and there were ritual ceremonies connected with their putting on and off into which I shall not pry. Poor Cousin George Coigne, protesting now elaborately that "of course, nothing could have been more flattering—of course, I need not say how sensible I am of the honour—"; and then, with a veritable groan, he broke down with, "I say, Hermy, you know, this is uncommonly awkward for both of us"—and she hastened to assure him that she took all his sensibilities for granted, and that, so far as she was concerned, the less he expatiated on them the better. She said that she was not inclined to marry just yet, and that, when she did, she should not allow grandmamma to dictate to her. Let him consider Harriet with her now, and not vex himself with grandmamma's absurdities.

Thus she calmed the agitated gentleman, who grew extremely docile all at once, and took the law as she laid it down. Harriet, she told him, was very well disposed towards him, but for her sake he must do nothing rash.

Oh, upright judge! Nothing could have pleased him better. "No, no, by Jove! you're right there—nothing abrupt, eh? Spoil everything—leave all that for the present. Play what we call the Fabian game—eh?" He saw himself a Fabius, wearing down Aunt Morfa by masterly impassivity.

On one point, though, Hermia was firmer than he relished. If her grandmamma spoke to her about it, she should tell the truth.

"What, all of it—eh? Would you do that, do you think?" cried Fabius.

"Yes, all of it—so far as it concerns me. Of course, I shan't speak of Harriet."

"Good Lord, no!"

"No. But I shall say that you have spoken to me, and that I have told you it's out of the question."

He shook his head. "She won't like that, Hermy. That's not her country at all."

"I'm very sorry—but what else can I do?"

He looked at her sideways. "Well—you could say, you know, that you were thinking it over—turning it about in your mind. That's what I should say—like a shot."

"But I'm not turning it about."

"Oh, of course, of course—naturally—the thing's absurd. But—Miss Harriet's awkwardly placed, don't you see?"

"I can't tell a fib, Cousin George—really, I can't do that." He took off his hat to her.

"Hermy, you are splendid, by George! You make me feel a—young hound, 'pon my soul. And I do hope you'll forgive me for troubling you with these affairs of mine—and believe that I put them all in your hands with—a great deal of pleasure, by Jove!—and confidence, and all that. I don't know what to do for the best—except that I must see Miss Harriet. Yes, I must see her, cost what it may. When I think of what she has to put up with—there—in that great black house—with that nodding old woman—Oh, Lord!" He shut his eyes for a moment. "Look here," he said, when he had opened them again, "I'll go to her now—I declare I don't care a curse—I beg your pardon, Hermy."

She was sorry for him, and said, "Let me go to her first—speak to her first. Trust me to help you all I can."

"I'd trust you with my immortal soul," said Sir George, feeling sure that he had one. And then he kissed her hand, and allowed Mrs. Moth to resume possession.

Lady Morfa had nothing to say to her granddaughter of any disposition made of her hand or heart; but Harriet, it appeared, had a great deal to say—and a great

deal more than she had been able to say so far. Harriet
knelt at Hermia's knees and wept; Harriet kissed and
clung; and at last she made a clean breast of everything—or so it seemed. But it is to be remarked of her
that all her confessions had had the air of finality about
them, as if they exhausted the subject.

"Oh, I was very wicked—I know—I know—" she
wailed. "He paid me marked attentions"—this, of course,
was Lord Morfa—"and I was pleased—very pleased. It
made me feel stronger, more able to bear—I was nobody
here—and her ladyship treated me like a servant.
Hermy!" her eyes were looming, "how would you like to
be called Chambre? I was always Moon—it made me
shiver. So then—I must tell you—I used to know when
he was coming—or going—and we used to meet. And
when he was kind to me, I felt altogether grateful and
couldn't refuse him what he—what we—what I told you,
Hermy, he did to me. I never loved him—no, I vow that
I did not; and all is over now between us—yes, all, all!
He was very fitful; sometimes I thought he was interested in me—especially when he came down to Petersham,
and left Lord Drem, and asked me to show him the
guinea-pigs—and—what I told you before happened.
But then—very often—he seemed not to remember me
at all. And now he's gone—and I declare that I am
glad. Oh, it's better so—much better—for me."

"I think so too," said Hermia, rather drily. "I fancied
that we were to talk of Sir George."

"Sir George was different," Harriet said composedly. "Sir George always acted towards me like a prince. But—" and she hid her face again, "oh, but Lord Morfa *was* a prince!"

"Very much a prince," said Hermia.

Harriet looked up, vehement and white. "It is all quite over. He cares nothing for me. I know where he goes— I know everything—I tell you, everything. Don't ask me any more."

"No, indeed, my dear," said Hermia. "Lord Morfa has no interest for me."

"Sir George is very kind," said Harriet, presently. "Any girl would be proud—" and then she burst into tears and implored her darling Hermy to temporise with Lady Morfa—which was precisely what had been re-fused to Sir George. But Harriet's argument, that a girl in her position must be very careful, was a strong one. If she were to run away with Sir George, said Harriet, how could he respect her any more? How could she respect herself? Hermia, child of runaway parents though she were, had no respect for that form of marriage. Why run away? But when she remembered the Fabian Sir George, and looked, not without some contempt, on the deplorable Harriet, she saw that no other marriage was open to them. She consented, finally, to temporise with her grandmother—to this extent that she would reply to any commands of hers that nothing could be done until she was out of mourning for her brother. Harriet's gratitude for so small a concession seemed disproportionate; and, after all, no temporising was called for. Lady Morfa had methods of her own which did not recognise a Fabian policy.

CHAPTER XXIII

BUT her own affairs now called to her, with urgent need of her championship. At the end of February she fell ill of the influenza, and had so much fever that she took to her bed, and consoled herself with "Marmion" and her violets. I don't know that she was, by ordinary, a great reader of poetry; but I am very sure that at this time she was a great maker of it. I shall not attempt to relate all the pretty, foolish pranks she played with her daily gift; they were doubtless much as maidens of old had used. When, for instance, Campaspe had the boy-god on her lap, and no one by, I trow she fondled him and coaxed for a wound; or when Lesbia and her sparrow sat alone, were the kisses less instant? So if Hermia played with her violets and lived with them a life of faëry, who's to wonder, or to blame? They made fragrant both her waking and her sleeping hours, crimsoned all her dreams of day and night. It may well have been during this time of quickened senses and imagination fever-fed that she staked her heart upon the issue which was now so near.

I say that she indulged herself—and she did when she made of her own will the admission to Harriet Moon which had been drawn out of her by the constancy of Tom Rodono. Harriet sat with her a good deal, and noted the violet-play with a very perspicacious eye. The flowers were never drawn from the bosom and laid upon the lips, to be returned presently and hidden in their nest, but Harriet saw the manœuvre and wisely smiled. But what she knew, or may have known, or may have guessed, she did not say. She hovered about them after her manner—"Darling, your flowers console you?" she would ask, and if Hermia, violets at her mouth, smiled behind them, or smiled with her bright eyes, Harriet would nod and look wise—and presently she would sigh. "You should be happy, dearest, I think—to be loved so long."

To this, on one day or other, Hermia answered, "I am perfectly happy. I believe I want no more of life than this."

"But He will want more," said Harriet, and Hermia, dreamy, asked, "He? Who is he? Are you—is it—sure that your He is not a she?"

Harriet said that she was sure. "Then I am not," says Hermia, "and what is more, I don't wish to be. If I am loved, and can love, what more do I need?"

This was rubbish, but Harriet did not say so. She asked presently whether her dearest friend had ever thought who it was that loved her so secretly, and whom it was she loved? Yes, said Hermia, she had thought.

"And you know nothing?"

She was snuffing at her flowers, but her eyes were steady
on her friend. "I know nothing certainly; nothing I
could talk about."

"And yet you are—in— Oh, Hermy!"

She admitted it. "Yes, I am in love, but I don't know
with whom—not certainly."

"But—dearest—I don't at all understand you now."

"How should you?" said Hermia—then she held up her
flowers. "He has sent me these for nine months. I cannot
but be grateful, I cannot but be humble to such a lover
as that. I am grateful—I love him dearly. I am
humble—I would obey him in everything. No one in
the world has ever been loved like this—in the dark."
Then she remembered. "Yes, there was one woman who
was loved in the dark. Her name was Psyche."

"A fable, darling! Psyche is the soul."

"Well," said Hermia, "and haven't I a soul?"

Such talk—of souls and their love-affairs—was highly
unprofitable to Harriet Moon; she was rather shocked,
rather scandalised. No confession she had ever made of
love-lorn baronets or kisses given and received before
guinea-pigs could be so damaging as this.

"Dearest Hermy," she said, "you make me unhappy. I
entreat you to reflect."

"I have reflected, my dear," said Hermia. "I am re-
flecting now."

"No, indeed, you are not. You are kissing your violets."

"They kiss me."

"This person," said Harriet, "have you never thought? It might be anybody—quite undesirable. Surely, surely, you see."

She nodded. "I do see—that you can imagine it being somebody impossible. You think it might be—Progers, for instance—or one of the men-servants?"

"No, darling, you wrong me. I think nothing so absurd. But I do think—" She paused. Yes, she must say it. "I do think that—possibly—it might be—young Mr. Vernour!"

Hermia, who was in a stare, did not answer immediately; but she laid her violets on the bed. "Yes," she said, "I have thought of that. I have wondered. Some day I may ask him. But it makes no difference that I can see."

"No difference! Dearest!"

"None at all. Either one loves or one doesn't; either one is loved, or is not. And if one is loved in so beautiful a way that must mean that the lover is noble. And if one loves—even if one loves an impossible person, as you say—if one loves with all one's heart, and is grateful, and is humble—there can be no harm. At least, I can see none."

Harriet stooped over the bed and embraced her, held her close in her arms. "Darling, tell me all! You love Mr. Vernour. You do! I know it." Hermia kissed her.

"You should be told if I could tell you. I love the

giver of my flowers—and have loved him since October. Perhaps longer; but it was in October that I knew it for certain."

"In October?"

"Yes. When we came back to town—and you brought me my flowers—and I was glad." She stirred in Harriet's arms, and snuggled down. "I cried," she said in a whisper, "and kept them with me all night. They have never left me since." And then she took them up, kissed them, and put them in her bosom.

Hermia knew, though Harriet did not, that Mr. Vernour was still in London. Moth had brought her that news—that he had inquired how she did, and that he inquired every day. On one occasion he brought her some flowers—purple and white anemones—which he told Moth were from his mother "for Miss Chambre, with her respects," and came from Feltham. She remembered presently that he had a friend there—a nursery gardener—and that he used to ride the chestnut thither on Sundays. A message was sent to him by Moth that she thanked him for calling, and begged her kind love to Mrs. Vernour.

He no longer called for orders, Moth said, as he had retired from business, and was intending for the country. He came "like a gentleman," she said, and described his appearance as being very like that of the Prince of Wales—but not so plump. He still came, of course, to the tradesman's door; but Moth had heard that he was becoming a great politician, and had spoken at a Westminster meeting with "Sir Francis and the Honourable Captain Ranald, and others of the nobility—all in favour of Reform, miss, and what a shame it was." When she recovered herself sufficiently to go downstairs and see company, she heard of that Westminster meeting—from Mr. Ranald. There had been a great to-do; they talked of prosecuting Sir Francis.

She asked him, Had Vernour spoken?

"Yes," he said, "and well. We should like some more of his sort. He's one of those men who say little and imply much. And he knows his power and how to husband it. He's for a waiting game."

"I am sure he's very strong," she said.

"If he is," said Ranald, "he owes it to you."

"To me?"

"To no other. He began to speak in public after that trouble of his, in which, if you'll let me say it, you played a fine part. I should like to put it that he saw, from what you did, that a cause which could breed such an act was a cause worth talking about. And though he's no great talker, as I say, he makes a fine show. He can restrain himself. He's a gentleman."

"I am sure that he is," said Miss Hermia.

Having ascertained from Moth that Vernour had gone into the country, beyond all doubt, she felt that she might safely pay a visit to Brook Street; and so she did, taking Harriet with her. The lady received her with great simplicity, and talked at length about her remarkable son. He had received a handsome offer from Lord Sandgate of a grazing farm in the Avon Valley, and was now gone down to inspect it. There was little doubt but that he would accept it. His father was willing, and David had never been happy in business. His heart was in the land, and in books. As for politics, no doubt he was for Reform; but Mrs. Vernour hoped that he would lose his zest for public speaking.

"He's quick-spirited, Miss Chambre, and means what he says. And he makes enemies, I fear. Captain Ranald, who is his best friend, makes them, too; but people will take from a lord's son more than they will from a tradesman. They say, It's only his fun, of such as Mr. Robert; but of my boy, they judge that he's bitter—which is far from the truth. He will be sorry to have missed your visit, Miss Chambre, really sorry. He thinks—he never forgets what you did for him." At parting, she took leave to congratulate the young lady. "I hear talk of a wedding, Miss Chambre—and a great ball that is to come. I hope that I may wish you joy."

Hermia laughed. "My grandmother, you mean. You must wish her joy of the ball."

CHAPTER XXIV

THE Countess of Morfa's ball, "to have the honour of meeting His Royal Highness," was fixed for the fifteenth of April, and was to be preceded by a banquet of forty persons carefully and rigidly selected. Each assembly in its kind was to be such as comported with the greatness of the house of Caryll; but collectively the two were to be more. They were to declare to the world the alliance which her ladyship contemplated, the marriage of Miss Hermia Mary Chambre with Sir George Coigne, Bart., of Plashetts, in Bucks, which she had decreed. And the great world so understood it to be, without any official announcement in the *Morning Post*. Whether Lady Morfa had her doubts of her granddaughter's docility, or whether, perhaps, she had no doubts, I cannot say: all that I know is that she spoke not one word to the young lady mostly concerned of the plans she had made in a matter vitally interesting to most young ladies. Miss Chambre, as we know, had her own opinion by this time of love and marriage and such-like, and had come to a very clear understanding with Sir George Coigne. She would, therefore, have viewed with great calm these elaborate preparations to herald an event which could never by any possibility occur, if her private and curious affairs had not made them of singular moment to her. But as these were, she was strangely uneasy and excited by a certainty which she had that this particular day and this particular party were to bring her sharply to a crisis.

At half-past six on the evening of this day she was in her dressing-room and in the hands of Mrs. Moth. Her coiffure was nearly done, for Moth had been deft over the coiling and curling of the most beautiful hair in London, as she heartily declared it. The Greek fashion was then in vogue—a high top-knot, with broad fillet to hold it, side curls, and—for this occasion—stiff white feathers must be added; for the court demanded them. This, I say, was nearly done: her dress of black and silver lay over a chair; her silver scarf with it—in a moment or two more she must stand up to be dressed; but in the meantime she sat with her thoughts—wondering and searching into the warm dusk for any sign which might reveal whither and with whom she journeyed.

This haunted, wonder-charged journey, which she had been making in secret places for so long, had changed of late. Formerly, she had wandered without rule or purpose; but there had been times when the world about her seemed real again; when the men and women with whom she talked, whose hands touched hers, were able to affect her with pleasure or distress, with admiration or

disgust.   They had at least as much claim to reality as
those shrouded, flitting forms which peopled her dream-
world.   Thus she had been able to be sorry for Sir
George's perplexities, and to be grieved by Harriet's
sobbed confessions, to be kind to Tom Rodono, and
moved by the force of Bob Ranald.   But now—of late—
all these had receded further and further into the mists.
She could still hear their voices, muffled and far-off;
still see, or think to see, their foolish, peering, staring,
agitated faces as they bobbed up and down in assembly—
but they were nothing, they were dreams of old days,
ghosts like her father and mother and poor Dick, unprofitable, touching, unavailing memories.   Really and
actually now she was living terribly, sweetly, in a secret
companionship—sought out, wooed by an unknown lover,
who now had won her and was about to claim his wages.
She thought that she was being led, now, at this dusky
hour of what, in the old world, men called the fifteenth
of April—was being led, as by the hand, from court to
court of some wonderful, empty house.   She could have
described to you—if you had suddenly startled her with
the question—the walls and coffered ceilings, the arch-
ways and pavements and flowers and fountain-basins of
this windowless house; she could have told you of the
long journeying and of the certainty which awaited her
at the end of it.   She could not see who guided her; she
could only feel, not see, the strong hand in which her
own lay contented.   There was no one visibly beside her;

yet one was there, and had her in an invisible hand. No
voice spoke to her: there was no need of speech when
her heart held the certain sense. "Come, my bride, this
house is thine and mine. This is the house of love, and
the hour of it has come upon thee."

Words of terrible sweetness they were: she had heard
them all day, and had not dared to answer, "Yes, I will
come. See, my lord, I am here: do with me as thou wilt."
No voice had he who spoke, and she needed none to
answer. Shy as a bride, and glad in her own beauty,
which had found such favour, she paced slowly the empty
rooms, that fair house, with downcast eyes and glowing
cheeks. She had no thought of drawing back; she was
passive now. Striving, daring, contending in the world
were all done. She had reached that point where the
woman gives over, is possessed; and her heart swelled
with the pride of perfect surrender to the sovereign will.

The chatter of Moth, the quick-glancing, quick-
fingered tire-woman, was like the twitter of sparrows in
the eaves to one who watches through the dawn for some
one to come home. If she heard it, she had no heed for
it. My lord, said Moth, had returned. What lord?
Why, my Lord Morfa, of course—what other lord had
Moth?—my lord had returned to town with the Prince,
and would be here to receive His Royal Highness. It
appeared, however, that his lordship would not dine—in
fact, he had sent word by Mr. Pigott, his servant, that
he was unavoidably detained. This was extraordinary—

in Moth's opinion. Her ladyship had said very little, but everybody knew that she was much offended: her ladyship said least when she was most offended, as everybody knew. Moth took upon herself to commiserate Miss Moon, who must now be enduring her ladyship at her worst. A place had to be filled at the last moment—and Miss Moon, it was understood, had been bidden to send for Mr. Banks. Mr. Banks? Who was Mr. Banks? Why, surely Miss Chambre would remember that sallow, thin gentleman with black nostrils—"like open graves," said Moth—whom Miss Chambre had met on a coach and asked to the house. Her ladyship esteemed Mr. Banks, Moth believed, and made him useful "in the newspaper way." He had influence, they said; he was listened to; and, of course, he would do anything for her ladyship. This was a great day for Mr. Banks. Was he coming? Why, of course he was coming. She should hope so. It was a command—to meet His Royal Highness.

To these facts of more or less importance Miss Chambre gave no heed. It may be doubted whether she heard them; and certain it is that she did not appreciate her Uncle Morfa's absence from the banquet as, say, Miss Harriet Moon would have done. Her thoughts held her in thrall. She was living elsewhere and apart; walking in invisible company, led by an invisible hand to her sure and certain destiny.

Prevision, second-sight, fore-knowledge, whatever you choose to call it, may be guessed at. Yet, when she found

herself convinced, as she had found herself ever since
her admissions to Harriet Moon, that her time was at
hand, she had had something to go upon, some rough
logic of the head to support, if that were needed, the
infallible sophistry of the heart. Those admissions had
been made some two weeks ago, but every day and every
night following upon them had but added to her certainty that her fate overshadowed her. Her flowers had
come exactly as usual—at the same hour, by the same
hand. She had untied them herself, and every time she
did it she had separated the stalks with trembling fingers
which expected momentarily to light upon some written
word lying concealed. But there had been nothing at
all; and here she had found the ground of her inference,
or ground for many.

If the giver of her violets were near her, in London,
say; if, indeed, he lived at all and could learn the things
that concerned her, then he must know by common
rumour what this fifteenth of April imported for her and
her affairs. And if—she reasoned—if this night and its
violet-gift passed without a sign, he (supposing that he
lived at all) must surely know that he would have no
further right to send her flowers, as men and women
judge these things. For men and women say that to
send flowers daily to a maiden is a declaration of love,
and to send them daily to a plighted maid is the act of
a robber.

The thought had smitten her suddenly one day, Say

that from the fixed night he ceased to send them, what should she do—now that he had brought her to this pass? Now that she had given herself; was, as she verily believed, handfasted to him? For was she not? Her flowers had lain in her bosom all night, and night after night; her flowers and all that they signified to her, which was more than any mere flowers could ever signify. They had been free of her lips, her tears, her breast, and her side; and not without disgrace, only as a maid un-done could she now stand before the world; as one who had suffered love and repaid love with love, and was now forsaken—like Psyche, like Psyche who had also loved and been loved in the dark. She pictured herself dis-mayed and forlorn, wandering footsore, dishevelled, with a bleeding heart, the streets, the squares, the parks of London, looking for the Unknown who had taught her love, betrayed, shamed, and left her. These were hot and incredible thoughts: yet were he mortal man or god such must be her portion if the only sign vouchsafed her were the ceasing of her flowers.

And if, in spite of a declared engagement, they did not cease to come, and she must learn by that that this lover of hers was not a mortal man at all, then how terrible was her destiny, how strange, how sweet! What must happen to her then—to her, the free, the proudly con-fident, the clear speaker of truth and well-spring of honour? How could she appear as wife, who had a secret lover? How could she give to a husband, a man, that right which the god in flower-shape had had of her and still chose to claim? She must remain unmarried, could not dare to marry. It would be mortal sin. Maids before now have had strange lovers: Oreithyia was mated to the North Wind, and one had a river to husband, and one a swan—it had remained for her, Hermia Mary, to discern the overshadowing which all women love and dread in the woody scent of wet flowers. . . .

To this strange state of mind was she now brought, and under the stress and fever of it now she suffered herself to be dressed.

It grew dusk apace, but she would not have the candles; so in half lights the shimmering gown was slipped over her head, the fillet and the scarf put in place. With vague eyes she stood up, searching the misty eve as it gathered about the trees in the garden, while the maid hovered over her, patting and adjusting, peering and judging, turning her about before the glass. Completed, adorned to the last hook and eye, she stood up, a picture of delicate, serious beauty, a bodily perfection of white and pale rose, which her black robe made to seem fragile as the petals of a flower, informed, however, by a mystery not of the world, which held together her sober lips and filled her large eyes with dark. Nothing remained to be done to her but to fix her flowers: let Mrs. Moth now see to that.

They were in a glass of water on the table, still untied; for on this crowning day, when all must be put to the touch, she had not dared yet to search them. The sign must be there to-day, or—nay, but it must needs be there. And yet so much hung upon that need that she had not dared to see. And as Moth was busy with them now—a pin in her mouth, and eager fingers at the tie—she felt herself grown white to the lips, and sick with the waiting and the fear. . . .

"My word of honour! Oh, miss!" It was over. The blood surged back and beat at her temples. He had spoken; the sign was there!

"Oh, miss! What next, I say! Oh, miss—" Words failed her, but she held up a folded slip.

"Give it me, please," she said steadily, not looking at it, and took, opened, and read it. She held it high to get the light, and while she read, Moth fixed and was pinning the flowers.

"This night, and for ever. Or nevermore."

That was the whole of it. It steadied her.

She freed herself from Moth's fingers. "Take them out, Moth, please. Put them on the table, and leave me. I shan't want you any more." Wondering, the maid unfastened the bunch, and while her mistress stood at gaze in mid-floor, her slip of paper in her hand, she returned to the table to lay it down. Suddenly she gasped, and said sharply, "Lord have mercy upon us! who's that?"

Hermia awoke from her trance. "Of whom do you speak? What do you mean?"

Moth chattered to herself, and peered out of the window. She could only say, "Down there—in the garden—alone. There's some one there. Oh, miss, you know best, but I tell you that I'm afraid."

Hermia, who wore a fixed face, went to the window and looked out. The garden was murky in the dusk of a warm April day; yet there could plainly be seen the tall and motionless figure of a man, cloaked and hatted, who stood alone there on the lawn. For a few moments she watched him, trembling. Then she motioned the maid to go away, and Moth retired without a word.

Hermia was shaking now, and panting, but she was not frightened. What unnerved her was the coming of the moment of choice, expected, and with certainty, so long. It had come. The Unknown Lover was there, the unknown country at the door, the journey must begin. She stretched out her left hand to touch the dressing-table, and it fell upon the softly crisp heads of violets. She took up the bunch in her hand, but it fell to her side. "This night, and for ever. Or nevermore." She knew what that meant; that it was for her to choose. Trembling, failing at the knees, breathless, in distress, with a crying pain at her heart, she watched and waited, while the room grew darker and darker, and the garden below could hardly be seen. She looked to the place where she had seen her lover stand, searched for him, found him, lost him again, until her eyes felt on fire. If she wore his violets that night, she was sealed to be his.

Would she do it? Dared she? Why, was she mad! She believed that she would be worse than mad—impious—if she disobeyed.

A knock at the door made her start and clap a hand to her side. "Who's there?"

Harriet opened the door. "Dearest, what's this? Why are you in the dark? Are you not ready? Her ladyship has sent me for you. Lord and Lady Crowland are here. They say that Sir Francis has been arrested and taken to the Tower. And oh, Hermy, Lord Morfa——"

"Go away, please," said Hermia, in a whisper. "Go down and say that I'm coming." Harriet pouted, but obeyed.

She must act at once; there was no time to lose. Disobedience never entered her head; all her hesitation had been that of a swimmer by the brink of the flood. She struck a match and lighted two of her candles with a steady hand. She had calmness enough at command to wait while the wicks flared, sank, and catching the wax, rose serenely into power. Then she pinned the white violets at her bosom, and, a candlestick in each hand, went deliberately to her window and stood there.

She stayed a few minutes facing the dark; then turned and went downstairs. She had sealed her indentures, was now bound apprentice. And as she went down the broad stair her heart seemed to fill her whole body, even to drowning her.

CHAPTER XXV

IN WHICH HER CALL COMES

A PRIEST newly from his altar-rites, with the dew of sacrifice still upon him, set down in the midst of some squalid brawl—contested election, city meeting—might have the feelings of consternation and dismay which possessed Miss Chambre, fresh from her window and her dark, seethed in the great Morfa banquet. And he would have the same consolation of hugging to his heart the memory and the promise known fully to him alone. If his eyes were wide and very bright, if his lips were close, if his tongue refused him, it were no wonder. In his eyes the vision would stay; mystery would lock his mouth and keep his tongue from declaring vain things. The apprentice in love went through the ceremony of dining in the company of forty persons, all fashionable and all Whigs; she gave her arm to Sir George Coigne, smiled on Lord Sandgate, curtseyed to a prince of the blood, tasted soup, sipped wine, answered questions, seemed, indeed, to be present, and looked excessively beautiful—though she was not very responsive. She was living elsewhere, at a fever-rate, in a shrouded garden, in still night air—or she was swept along a flooded stream, in water which was warm and sweet—in which her limbs failed her, in which, drifting, she drowned. Swift, smooth, irresistible motion; she was conscious mostly of that. Her hands were folded, her eyes closed, she felt; she knew not whither she went, and cared nothing. For above and about her, fanning her brows, blowing upon her eyelids, was a form whose magnitude she could not guess—and "Come. I have chosen thee; come. Thou art mine, and I am thine—now and for ever," was the music in her ears.

What, then, if a royal personage should enunciate laws of nature at the top of his voice and the table? She would not hear them. "I tell you, ma'am, the country was never more respected abroad. Our good old King, secure in the sanctities of family life . . . what?" "My brother Kent, ma'am, may be trusted to fulfil his duty, I hope. Church and King is the cry . . . the nobility staunch, the Commons . . ." Oh, crackling of thorns under pots! What had she to do with Lords and Commons?

Mr. Aloysius Banks, with a crowing voice, might have been heard blaring loyalty over the board. "What said Mr. Burke, sir? What said that true patriot? 'We fear God—we look with awe to kings—with affection to Parliaments—with duty to magistrates—with reverence to priests—and with respect to the nobility.'" That should have been gracious to a royal ear, and likely was; and it should have been interesting to watch Lady Morfa's nodding head receive it. "With awe to kings"

—she bowed low; "with reverence to priests"—she raised her eyebrows as her head made the concession; "and with respect to the nobility"—she tossed her feathers upwards before her final inclination. It was very right that these should be the opinions of the Burkes and Bankses of this world, but almost an affectation of humility for a Lady Morfa to agree with them.

Lord Sandgate capped Mr. Banks with Tom Paine, for the benefit of his beauteous neighbour. "The duty of man . . . a wilderness of turnpikes, through which he is to pass by tickets!" You are a Painite, I know, Miss Chambre. Was she? She smiled upon him and allowed him to believe it. Had there really been a time when she had been this or that? Lord Sandgate talked of Sir Francis, whom he had that morning escorted to the Tower, at the head of some thousands of frantic persons. "You would have said it was a Roman triumph, Miss Chambre; and I'm inclined to think that it was. At least the Government can only afford a few more such victories. Bob Ranald came back rubbing his hands. He says nothing could have been better. If privilege strains so far, it will snap—and suicide is better than assassination; more decent at least." And so he ambled on, the contented nobleman, and she said Yes, or No.

Upon her other side were Sir George and his troubles. He felt fatally prominent, and feared to commit himself deeper with every breath. He knew what that

offer of his arm was to imply, and what the whole
festival implied. He sat at meat a marked man. From
the crimson flock walls, out of their gilt cornices,
from beneath their coronets, the ranked Carylls in
their purple and ermine, their shimmering satin, in their
full wigs, lace collars, ruffs, steel corselets, peak-bearded,
love-locked, ample-bosomed, fiercely stayed and hooped,
as the case might be—a double row of Carylls
watched him out of level, unfaltering eyes. He was
not an imaginative man, but he fairly cowered. God
in heaven, what was he doing, this free-dealing, friendly
baronet of Plashetts? Was he a man? Why did he
not break away, and seek out his love? His heart
was out of the room in the thin hands of a lady—a
brown-eyed slip of a girl, with a piteous mouth and
courteous ways. Oh, he should be by her side, braving
the world—but here he was, drinking brown sherry and
saying, "Yes, sir," to a royal duke. Out upon him,
recreant! "Hermy, you stand by us—eh? This is hot
work, you know. I'm all for peace and quiet, you know—
that's how a man gets through his day's round. By
heaven, I never bargained for this." She was gentle with
him, poor creature though she saw him.

"You will see Harriet in the ball-room. She is to be
there, I know."

"Watched, though! Tied hand and foot! Gad, what
a life for a lovely—I say, Hermy, what shall we do for
her? This is awful!"

Was this a man? Oh, if he only knew, if he only knew where, with whom she stood now! "Really, Cousin George," she broke out, "I cannot understand you. You are your own master, dependent upon nobody, and yet— You have but to ask her—surely you see that?"

He shook his head desperately. "Can't have a fuss, you know, Hermy. Never do. Aunt Morfa's head of the family—our family as well as yours—not actually, of course, because Uncle Badlesmere's the man; but she's older than him by a deal, and she's always had her own way. No, no—can't break with the family if we can avoid it. Why, bless my soul, my mother was the youngest of eleven!"

"You talk as if we were all children together."

"Well, there's that, of course—I see your point. But the family—no, no. We must think of something better than a fuss."

"A fuss! Why should there be a fuss?" She simply had no more to say. Sir George sighed, and went back to his dinner.

"Where's Morfa?" Lord Sandgate enquired. "Wasn't he to be here?" He was told the facts about Lord Morfa.

"My lady won't like that."

"She doesn't. One can see that she doesn't." One could.

"I think that Morfa should be pulled up—indeed, I do.

He's wild—he's in a wild set. He's a fool, saving your respect, but he's not bad all through. One of these days he'll be caught hold of—by a woman. And that'll save him." She thought of Harriet; and as the ladies rose and left the dining-room that thought went with her, mingled with her own. Harriet, too, might have her wondrous secret life; on Harriet's pale lips, on Harriet's brown eyes the mystery might have been laid. Entering the ball-room, last of a long procession, the first persons she saw were Lord Morfa, making his bow to the Duchess of Wentsland, and Harriet Moon, flushed and downcast, standing by her patroness. Had these two been together long? Was this why he had refused to dine?

Among the gentlemen, where Archdeacon Caryll had taken the host's chair and was beaming, speechless and helpless, upon his rapidly intoxicating Prince, a painful ordeal was in process. Sir George Coigne had been called up to the right of the great personage, and was receiving congratulations upon his approaching marriage. The lady was approved, in terms more warm than agreeable. "His Royal Highness's expressions," said the Archdeacon afterwards, "were not lacking in ardour. They testified to the—ah!—vivacity of his sensibilities; but they did not, my dear Jane, show that delicacy of touch for which the heir to the throne is so deservedly beloved." Sir George owned to an intimate friend that he had never felt worse in his life. "Damn it, those princes, you know—what? They give a twist—

eh? Must have mustard with their mutton—cayenne on their buttered toast. It's all very well, my dear Clare, but that sort of thing sickens a man. I shall bolt for Gretna—I'll be shot if I don't."

"Will the lady go, George?"

"I know, I know," said Sir George, wringing at his nail, "and there's the racket: family racket, county racket. Too much to ask of any girl—eh? That's what I feel about it."

"Depends on her, of course," says the youthful Clare, prematurely wise. "I should have said that Miss Hermia——"

"Oh, bless you, *she'd* go—like a bird. Why, she's said so! But not with me, my boy; not with me." He spoke in a whisper, behind his wine-glass.

"Oh! Beg pardon," said his friend. "I thought she was the lady."

"So you might, God knows! But if she ain't? Not many girls would face what my Cousin Hermy would—and think nothing of. Nor should she be asked, in my opinion. But I'm talking!"

"Not at all, George, not at all," his friend assured him. "Naturally, it goes no further."

"God Save the King" in the great hall made the gentlemen move. "God bless me, have we sat so late? That's my brother," cried the great man. He was got to his feet, and swayed out into the gallery to meet his Prince.

It was eleven o'clock when the Prince came—in semi-state. Six horses drew him instead of twelve, and it is possible that there was rather less hooting because there were rather fewer sightseers; but there was enough to render very necessary the services of a brass band which, for drowning purposes, had been ambushed in the court. When he entered the hall, with Lords Hertford, Conyngham, and Moira, with Mr. Sheridan and others of his friends, he was flushed and noisy, but not tipsy.

The Morfa clan and the Badlesmere clan received him in the inner hall, at the foot of the great stair. Her ladyship in Botetort emeralds and Caryll diamonds, Morfa with his garter—these were in the centre of the galaxy; and about them the tributary lights, a nameless, high-nosed herd of Gells, Coignes, Barwises, Lukyns, Botetorts, Carylls, and heaven knows who. Head above most of these there stood a troubled, rosy-faced baronet from Bucks—and beside her ladyship's self the grave, glowing, beautiful Hermia Mary, hot and deep as a ruby in her black and silver setting, with her knot of white violets rising and falling with her breast. So seriously she looked at her advancing Prince, you might have thought her his judge; so scornfully curved her lip you must have known it. What to her was the advance and boisterous cordiality of this overflowing personage, this young Silenus of creased eye-sockets, and of the colour of pink paint? Was she to curtsey, kiss the hand of this beribboned, fuddled, bloated man of forty—and her heart, her will and soul out there in the cedared garden, quivering under the calm eyes of a god?

But here he was, exceedingly disposed to make himself agreeable. "By God, Roddy, I'm late," he declared. "'Twas Moira kept me, I'll swear. Madam," and he looked heavily at Lady Morfa, "you must blame the wits, not me."

"Impossible, sir, to blame one without the other," said her ladyship, whose curtsey was a thing to ponder: the bared edge of a razor would not have been finelier avoided by a naked foot. But he was determined to be pleased, and sure that he pleased. "Ha, Mr. Archdeacon—ha, Badlesmere, this is a meeting of friends—all Whigs here, hey? We must have you at Carlton House, Badlesmere—we don't see enough of you. Lady Conyngham asked after you the other night; she did, upon my soul. Lady Barwise, I'm very glad to see you—very glad, indeed." He shook hands with Sir George and congratulated him effusively; begged to be presented, and when he saw the fair betrothed remembered her at once. "By my honour, the lovely Jacobin! Why, why, Miss Chambre and I are old cronies—we met—let me see—don't tell me that you forget it, young lady. And I've heard of you—where now? Moira, what was that I heard of Miss Chambre? Devilish good thing that was—Oho! I have it. Brook Street!—cleaving to the——By heaven, Coigne, you must keep your wife out of Brook

Street. No dealings with that firm—hey?" And on he rattled, perfectly satisfied with himself.

She made no answer, but leaned her cheek and let him touch it; she curtseyed deeply, and when he claimed her for a quadrille, did her part with a stiff recollectedness which piqued him not a little. She was moving, in fact, as one in a dream; and so she went through her duties of the night—dancing with this man and that: Tom Rodono, Lord Edlogan, the Honourable John, and the Honourable James, it mattered not a bit. In the midst of the blare and bustle, the loud voices of great men, the whisperings of men aspiring, and the bowings of those whose glory was to creep—catching sight of Harriet Moon at a window, and struck to contrition by her woe-begone look, she left her partner with an excuse, and went directly to her. Harriet saw her coming, and seemed to shrink. Hermia did not hesitate. "Harriet," she said, "have you anything to say to me?"

The brown eyes dilated, the pretty mouth faltered. "Anything to say? Oh, Hermy, why should I?"

"You are the best judge. Is all well with you?"

"Yes, yes, very well. Why do you ask me?"

"I feel anxious. I can hardly say why—but I have thought much of you. Will you not confide in me? I am your friend."

Harriet was moved, and seemed on the point of speaking—but she checked herself and looked down. "I think I have told you all," she said.

"All, Harriet?"

"Hush!" said Harriet. "Somebody is coming for you." A young man came up.

"I beg your pardon, Miss Chambre; Lady Morfa sent me to tell you that she is going down to supper. His Royal Highness has begged that you will honour his table."

"I'll come," said Hermia, and went away with him.

The inexpressible twenty minutes which followed may be passed over. If she had been in possession of herself, able to contrast her real and her unreal existence, the world in which her soul walked and that in which her body sat, it must have made her laugh aloud. She formed one of a table of six persons: the brother princes, who talked loudly, and tripped up each other's stories; Sir George Coigne, most miserable of men, searching the supper-room with strained eyes for his Harriet, who was not there; Lady Morfa, hardly at pains to conceal her contempt for the society she was in; Lady Badlesmere, steadily eating and drinking; and she, this secretly bewitched, secretly rapt, spell-bound, beautiful girl: was there ever such a supper-table? It was interrupted by an equerry, whose message, testily heard, proved urgent. The Prince swore heartily, but nevertheless got up and took his leave. The whole company rose, and with "God Save the King" and a prodigious pawing and scraping of horses, His Royal Highness was got on to the road. By that time Hermia had escaped.

She had observed that Lord Morfa, against all eti-
quette, had not been in attendance during supper, and
that Harriet was not to be seen either. Couple this with
his absence from dinner and presence in the drawing-
room—throw in the girl's abject look and refusal to
speak—all her suspicions came back: Harriet must be
found. She passed through the almost empty ball-room,
tried the card-room, the yellow saloon, oval drawing-
room, the library. Here she was assailed by a draught
of fresh, pure air which blew in from an open window.
Beyond that lay the balcony—beyond that the garden,
where her soul walked. Her own affairs possessed her
heart and mind, and, jealous of rivalry, usurped the little
corner in each where Harriet still held out.

She went out through the window, and immediately, as
it seemed, the blaring world of princes and crackling
thorns was shut out. The balcony was empty, the night
was before her, the enchanted garden, and the garden
gods. Her own thoughts resumed their realm, her own
body went prone to receive back her soul. She stood
wonderingly, face to face with the night.

Forthright she looked into the velvet dark, with beating
heart and parted lips, living at ease in the enormous
peace of the silence. After the glare, the glitter, and
the brawl, the lapping and supping, the crunching of
ortolans' bones, the leering looks and bragging tongues
—here, deeply in the violet night, beyond the trees, seen
only by the stars, the unknown lover abode, he who spoke

in the fragrance of flowers, and was the veiled Eros, the hidden spouse. She, Psyche, had given her pledge—and he might be here—he must be here—to claim it of her.

She was highly excited, but not afraid. Her breath was quick, but her eyes undimmed, her gaze constant and untroubled. She knew that she was not alone. He was there—and she sure of it. She stood and waited, holding her breath, holding the ledge of the balcony with her two hands. She stood for some moments thus, hearing the wild music of her heart. And then, out of the environing night she heard herself called—whether from near or far she did not know; she heard her own name, called twice—"Hermia, Hermia Mary."

She answered—not moving from her place—"I am here."

Now the speaker was nearer—but not to be seen. "You have decided? You have chosen?"

"Yes, yes. You know it."

"I may serve you still?"

"You know it."

"I would serve you for ever?"

"I am not worthy."

"I have served you for a year."

"Yes."

"You will hear me? At dawn?"

"Yes, I will come."

"I shall be here at dawn."

"I will come to you."

"You accept my flowers?"

"You know that I have accepted them."

"Stay no longer now. Good-night."

"Good-night."

She knew that he was gone; but she stayed where she was, motionless, possessed, and held.

CHAPTER XXVI

WHICH IS OF PSYCHE IN THE GARDEN

IT would not be an easy thing to describe the wave of high exaltation which carried Miss Hermia Mary to her bed and prevented her from sleeping in it. One might, perhaps, more surely gauge the consternation of a break-fast-table in far Kilbride when it received as a bolt from the blue heaven the letter whose writing occupied a good part of her vigil. For she slept not at all, but stood for near an hour at her window, drinking, as it were, the wonders of the night, lay wide-eyed upon her bed for another, in a state of warm, still acquiescence in her fixed destiny, and after that composed the extraordinary letter from which I am about to quote.

"It is right that I should tell you first of all the world, my dearest friend, that my affections are deeply engaged, even while, in the same breath, I have to confess that I do not certainly know the name of the object of them, and am not certainly aware that I have ever seen him. What I may guess, or what I may believe, it would not be proper to say; in a very few hours I shall know *all*— in the meantime, I know enough to assure you of this.

"I cannot tell what you will think of me, but I do believe that you will understand what I cannot explain,

and that your love will enable you to see as reasonable
what might appear incredible. I remember when we used
to have our twilight talks at dear Kilbride, we often
wondered together what my portion would be. We talked
of husbands—never of lovers; I don't know why. I used
to say that I should marry a soldier like dear papa—and
now—oh, it is most wonderful!

"Mary, I have been silently, mysteriously, and con-
stantly loved since the twenty-second of June last year.
That has been proved to me by such a service as no girl
can ever have had before; in such a way and by such
means that it is impossible to doubt either the sincerity
of my lover or the marvellous delicacy of his declaration.
He told me, however, but two hours ago, that he had loved
me for a year—that is, for I am sure he is incapable of
the smallest deviation from the truth, from the fifteenth
of April. That might give me a clue to his person—and
I do think that it does; but in such a matter you will not
ask me for surmises, but for certainties. My dearest,
I tell you two. The first is that I am beloved; the second,
Mary, that I love. I know now that I have loved him,
or his violets—for he sent me white violets, every day,
at the same hour—since October, when darling Dick
died. What a proof of sensibility in my lover, that on
the day when the dreadful news came my violets ceased,
and were withheld until I returned to town in October.
When I missed them, Mary, I was troubled without
knowing why; I could not understand why they should

mean so much to me. But in October, when they were renewed—when I found them here awaiting my return—and when I shed tears—happy tears of pride and gratitude—then, indeed, I understood well enough what had befallen me. I took my violets to my heart, I kissed them often, they never left me; I could not falter after that. I did it in spite of myself, and they became a part of myself, indispensable. No, indeed, I could not falter. Nor shall I falter when, in a few hours' time, as soon as the light begins, I go out of this house to meet my lover face to face—and *my* light begins!

"He spoke to me last night out of the dark. I was on the balcony; for I knew he was in the garden below, and went to him, and waited for him to speak. He called me by my name, twice. 'Hermia,' he called, and then 'Hermia Mary,' as if he knew that they who loved me best always called me so. I told him that there I was—taking all things for granted in a simple way which, I am convinced, could never be possible for any two persons who had not been drawn together by fate. He asked me to come to him in the morning, at dawn—and the dawn is just at hand, Mary; I can see the grey light in the sky; and at the first flush I go. When you receive this, you will pray for me—or, no; you will give thanks to God that your Hermia Mary is happy. Happy I shall assuredly be—for I am extraordinarily happy now—and proud to suffer whatsoever may be in store for me. I may be far from here—for if he calls me, I shall follow him; or perhaps I shall be locked up again, as I was, you remember, when grandmamma disapproved of me. I may have to endure even worse—I may estrange all my friends (except you!), make a scandal—I don't know. But I know this very well, that I shall never falter now, and never look back.

"Good-bye, Mary, my dearest friend! I wish that I might go out to my happy destiny strengthened by your kiss; but do you pray for me always, as I do for you, and I don't feel alone. . . . It is almost light, and I have not been to bed at all. How could I sleep? How can I rest? What need have I? Good-bye; the dawn is here!

                    "YOUR OWN HERMIA MARY."

Having sealed this letter, she made her preparations; rinsed her face and hands in cold water, put order to her hair, dressed herself, pinned her violets upon her, covered herself with a cloak and hood, and went quietly, but without any carefulness to be quiet, along the drowsy corridors, down the ghostly stair, through echoing halls and muffled saloons to the garden-door. This she must unbolt and unbar with difficulty. It was about five o'clock upon a still morning.

The shadowless grey light saluted her, the cool dawn air fanned her cheeks, and playing upon her, caused her to shiver and draw closer the cloak she had on. She shut the door behind her, not as yet daring to look for whom she knew to be awaiting her. So also, with lowered eyes, she went down the steps which gave to the terrace, crossed that, and descended the next flight, stood upon the grass, and waited there, not yet lifting her head, holding still the hems of her cloak close about her with a quiet hand. Her hesitation was momentary. She lifted a burning face, she looked forward with misty eyes. She saw a tall figure motionless in the shadow, by the cedar, and went staidly down to meet it.

He was cloaked and booted, but his head was bare. He watched her come, watched intently; his lips were pressed together, his eyelids did not blink. He was like a carven man whose regard is fixed as the sculptor willed it, whose thoughts are as unfathomable as you please because they must be your own. He did not move forward to meet her, nor bow his head, nor show any sign at all. And when she stood, as now she did, at some three paces away, her eyes were as firm and unwinking as his own. So each gazed at the other for some seconds—and then she gave up the strife, and looked down.

He spoke to her. "You have chosen to come—knowing what you knew?"

Her voice was very low. "I thought it your right."

"Right!" he said, "I have no rights but what I have had from you. And you have dared to give me another. You have dared, because you dare all things."

"No," she answered, "not all things. I must tell you— that I cannot receive your gifts—now that I know that they are yours—without confessing to you that I am grateful. I dare not do that. That is why I have come."

"I asked you," he said, "but I hardly hoped——" Then she looked at him again, for a moment—and presently spoke as if to herself.

"You must have known that I would come."

He seemed to have no answer ready, but stood as one whose mind is whirled about.

"I put everything to the touch—to win or lose—it was forced upon me. I could not last—could not endure. It was the act of a coward, of a desperate man—I thought that you must know by now—the truth was blazed on my face. I thought all London knew that the clown had lifted up his eyes to the highest. And so I reward your gracious act—your act of pure nobility——" he stopped with a cry of despair, and she made as if she would go to him.

"Don't accuse yourself, I beg of you—for I may not be able to tell you what I ought."

He had recovered his self-possession, and spoke quietly. "I will ask you to listen to me. It is all I have the right to ask you. I have loved you for a year since yesterday —since that day when, of your own generosity, you came to my poor house—where I was—disgraced—and approved and gave me back my manhood. From that moment of that day I was yours altogether; and I own to you that the fact in me was so proud and glorious a fact that I did not strive against it.   No, but I set myself to work to be worthy so splendid a state.   What harm could I do you—if you knew nothing of it? Who could deny me the right to bend my knee?   I tell you now that I rode about my business—mine, of all businesses in the world!—like a knight of old time shining in the sun. Had I stayed thus, could I have blamed myself? or could you blame me?"

Her lips moved to answer him, but he stayed her. "Not yet—not yet."

He continued: "I made no declaration then—and had I kept my senses I should never have made one.   I know that I fell away, was false to the glory of my beginning. But madness seized me.   You met me—you knew me again—you bowed your head—and, God help me! I lost mine."

Again she stopped him.   "You have no need to excuse yourself—pray——"   He held up his hand: "I beseech you!" and she begged his pardon.

"I do believe that when I made my sign—which meant what wickedness, what arrogance, what gross presumption you will—it was in such a way that you could not be compromised, could not feel yourself bound in any kind of honour to consider who it was who so declared himself.   You were free then, as you are now, to bestow your generosity as you please.   For even now I ask no more of you than leave to tell you the truth.   I do ask that—I must ask that.   Will you let me tell you?"

"Tell me," she said, whispering.

"The truth is this," he said, "that I love you and am your man. And now I am content to go, and never see you again."

He stood waiting, having dared his uttermost. The girl's dignity wrapped her closely. "I do not ask you to go. You must do as seems to you best—as seems right to you. I trust you entirely."

"You must not trust me," he said, "with such an answer as that. I am a man, and I love you. Do you hear me say that, and then give me leave to remain? To send you flowers?"

She was in great trouble now, though she bore it stilly. "I don't know how to answer you," she said; "I think you do me great honour." He saw that she was trembling; but pity does not enter into a man at such a time.

"Honour, as you understand it, as I believe it—it is not for me to say. All honour should be yours from all men—and yet love should be something. Is it nothing to you to be loved by a man? Then manhood and love are nothing. High-born as you are, delicate and rare, and sweet of blood as you are—faring softly—of a race unknown to mine—for all this, which you can never lose, I offer you a man's love. I am neither fool, nor knave, nor coward—and if you give me the right I will serve you before all your world, and claim you, too. And I will make bold to add this—that I will content you if you give me the right. What do you say?"

She could not answer.

"Hermia, what do you say?" She shivered a little, and folded her cloak about her.

"You must know what I must say," she said. "I am yours, and will come when you call me. I will go where you bid me. I will follow you over the world." Vernour took a stride forward; she held out her surrendering hand. He knelt on both his knees, and kissed it. Then he rose, bowed, and left her.

CHAPTER XXVII

UPON a time of wild elation, when her blood, thought, and senses were swirling together down a mill-race, Moth intervened, the bright-eyed and intelligent Moth, to see if she were stirring and would ride. It was eight o'clock.

"God bless me, miss!"

She took everything literally now. "Yes, yes, oh, Moth, he has blessed me."

Moth was alert in a moment. "It's to be hoped so, indeed, miss, though as a humble Christian I say it. Little enough we know of such things, save and except that women have the worst in the long of it. Your pardon, miss, but whoever have dressed you this morning?"

"I dressed myself—as you see."

"See! I could have seen it blindfold, miss, if you will excuse the liberty. Your hair! Miss Hermia, will you ride?"

"Certainly, I shall ride. But I should like some tea first, if you please. I am thirsty."

She was fed, she was dressed, and she rode out, her man behind her, into the blue and gold, the mist, the glory and tender promise of London April. It all seemed personal to her, she took it as a message, as an augury, the foolish child. Entering the park, she spurred her horse and galloped to her heart's content. Faster than four hoofs flew her high thoughts.

Tom Rodono, who, for her sake, forswore late hours and got himself into the saddle betimes that he might see and perhaps speak with her, watched her fly past him, veil and hair streaming like pennons behind her. A nymph of the chase! He was wrong. She was a nymph in chase, an unharboured deer.

She passed him more slowly the second time round, saw him, and reined up. Friends with all the world, she felt especially tender towards him. "What demon possesses you this morning?" he asked her. "You ride like a creature of the storm."

She felt that she must hold herself in check, lest she blaze her secret to the world. "I suppose it is that I am very well. At least, I have blown away the memories of last night."

"A great party! All the Whig world and all its wives."

"Is there a Whig world? I had forgotten it."

"There are more worlds in this old globe than you know of, young lady."

She laughed. "I suppose so. Yes—I am sure there are." She then found that she had been dealing with a world whose inhabitants were reduced to two.

They spoke of Sir Francis, capitulated and in the Tower. What was to come next? There was to be a great Westminster meeting—would she care to go? Bob Ranald was to speak—"and your man, Vernour." Her man, Vernour! She could have laughed aloud. Of course, she would go—of course, she must.

"It could be easily arranged," says Tom. "Grizel will take you, and I'll be in charge. You shall dine in Clarges Street, and we'll make a party."

She rode home to breakfast—to find her flowers, but no letter, no further sign. It was clear that she was to wait, say nothing, do nothing. Her first impulse had been to give battle to her grandmother; but she supposed now that he intended to do that himself.

Reaction followed hard upon her crowning hour; she became restless and miserable, not that she doubted him for a moment, but that her powers of endurance should be so frail, that her desire of sight, speech, and touch should be so overmastering, that her violets should be no comfort to her—these things frightened her. She felt lonely—like Ariadne whom the god Bacchus had loved for one burning hour, and then forsaken. She felt a traitor to what had been loveliest in her love—her happiness in the unknown lover, who was hidden in the woody fragrance of violets. Like Psyche, she had sought to see his face, and like Eros he had shone upon her, once, and now was gone.

She knew not what to do, in whom to confide. She went half-way to Brook Street to see his mother, but found

her resolution fail her, lest he should be there. Some
grain of pride left in her—which she felt to be her shame,
but could not ignore—bade her believe that she would
sooner die than seek him anywhere. Under these circumstances, she found her drill-routine of dinners, assemblies, routs, and balls unspeakably flat, until by chance
she met Mr. Robert Ranald, and learned that he would
talk, of his own accord, of Vernour. Apart from this
pleasing trait, she was not long in discovering that he was
worth listening to for his own sake; and she was a little
shocked with herself to find that she could be interested
in politics—in the fight at long odds which all whom she
had ever loved had been waging for so long as she could
remember. It savoured, to her, of disloyalty that she
could care for anything in the world beside Vernour.
Nevertheless, Mr. Ranald, or Captain Ranald, as he
actually was, approved himself to her sympathies as well
as her understanding.

He was in great spirits, as always when fighting uphill;
he smiled awry, wrinkled his forehead, chuckled, rubbed
his hands together. He had a burnt brown seaman's
face; his skin looked as if it had been strained taut with
keys—like a drum—and had cracked and slightly blis-
tered at the bones. He was very lean and very big-
boned, but exceedingly healthy.

He confessed to her now that he had a task on hand
which might very well put the capstone on his monument
of discredit. "Burdett is hated by Ministers," he said,

"whom he irritates, but the understrappers respect him because he's rich. Now, I'm poor, for a lord's son, so the smaller fry can afford to hate me; and they work on the others. Where Burdett goes to the Tower, they might have me in the pillory—and, perfectly honestly, I wish they would. It's a barbarous form of torment; but, by heaven, I should be the last man to have it!"

"My dear Miss Chambre," he said to her on one of these meetings of theirs, "you may thank God you were not born into the world with an eye for windmills. I'm not so sure, by the bye, that you were not—I seem to remember something." This made her laugh and blush. "It's very well to laugh," he said, "and I allow the sport is rare—but the thing gets on to the brain and breeds a maggot. Very soon it comes about that you see men as mills walking, and parade the streets of this town, lance in rest, looking for 'em. What on earth have I got to do with rotten boroughs and rogues in chief seats? Nothing in the world; my business is piracy. I went into the House as a seaman because I couldn't stand the fleecing of the finest fellows and direst fools in England by a set of Quaker scoundrels not fit to scrape their boots— and here I am dancing before King Mob in the hope of getting old Percival's head on a charger."

He spoke of Vernour, calling him, as Rodono had, "your man, Vernour." He thought he would go far. "He's got fire in reserve; he banks it. I think that he does you credit, and may do you more. I suppose you see nothing of him?" She admitted, not much. "Well," he said, "it so happens that I've seen a fairish deal. He's young—I dare say that he might be six-and-twenty— but he's capable, and his father is well off; so the young man has his freedom; he's a freeman of Westminster, one of my 'lambs.' The fact is that he behaved very well indeed in that business of your grandmother's—monstrous bit of tyranny that was, saving her presence. Before I knew you—before I had that honour of meeting you at Caryll House—Cobbett told me something of the case, and made my blood boil. I don't mind telling you now. Well, I was in more than two minds to raise a debate in the House about that affair; I suspected the very mischief was in it—Carlton House, York House, God knows what house. Windmills, my dear Miss Chambre— infernal things they are! Your man came to see me, and to beg me not to move. He made me some mystery, mentioning no names, mind you—said that ample amends had been done—not money, not a horse, not custom—far greater honour had been done him than that; he had received a gift beyond price, incalculable, *et cetera*. I confess, I didn't know then what the young man meant, but I do now. You made a man of him, Miss Chambre, and now he acts like a man. He's going to speak at our meeting—you'll hear him. He's educated himself— he's rough—but he has the soul of a gentleman—God bless me! what am I talking about?—he has the soul of a man." She was all in a glow; tears brimmed her eyes.

"The soul of a man speaks," was all that she could trust herself to say. He put up his hand.

"Don't flatter me. I'm a lunatic. My name is Bob Quixote."

"That was the name of a man and a gentleman," said she.

"Yes, we'll remember that. And mind you this: it's the fools who do the work of the world, and the wise who profit. So you may choose."

She looked serious and most beautiful. He observed her eyes and thought he had never seen any more wonderful grey light. She was like the Sibyl, new from commerce with the divine.

"I think I have chosen. I know that I have."

He smiled. "You join our company?"

"Oh," she said, "I shall be called a fool, most certainly."

She was to accompany the Clarges Street party to the Crown and Anchor meeting; she was to dine and sleep there. Lady Morfa had no care for the opinion of Westminster freeholders in any event, and her only stipulation was that Sir George Coigne should accompany the ladies. So he was to be included. Another person who intended to be present was Mr. Aloysius Banks, who had become of late very much the servant of Caryll House. Lady Morfa, finding him useful, had permitted him to take up the duties of jackal, and listened to him with a mixed air of amusement and contempt which she did not attempt to conceal. When he told her that he thought it his business to be there, she replied that she thought so too. "You are a philosopher, my good sir," she said, "and can only formulate wisdom out of the ravages of folly. Go by all means, and observe fools."

"Did your ladyship chance to hear," said Mr. Banks, "that the young man, Vernour, was to be one of the speakers?"

Her ladyship had not heard that, and was not sure that she remembered his name. So, at least, she said.

Mr. Banks enlarged upon Vernour. A young man of extreme opinions and dangerous license. The Government had him in mind. He had been befriended, he said, by persons of consequence—by Lord Sandgate, Captain Ranald, Sir Francis, and others of even greater rank. He went no further, because he saw that her ladyship was now perfectly aware of what he was saying; but he added that, in his own opinion, it was the business of all those whose ability to serve the State was the sole measure of their right to do so—of those who, like himself, pretended to no natural right—it was their business, he had been saying, to report scrupulously upon any symptom of irregularity in those wise provisions which, etc., etc. I have followed him further than his patroness already, and shall cut him short by her assistance.

"You mean," said Lady Morfa, "that you are going to take notes of what this young man says?"

"I conceive my duty to be so, madam, unless your ladyship——" He paused, expectant.

"My dear man," said her ladyship, "what do you suppose your conceptions have to do with me?"

CHAPTER XXVIII

WHICH REPORTS A WESTMINSTER MEETING

THEY arrived early, and sat in the front row of the gallery, six ladies all in black, with hoods and veils, and since Sir George at the last moment had cried off, only Tom Rodono to mount guard over them. Miss Chambre recalled to mind Lady Mary Wortley's description of a harem at the mosque. In course of time the veils were put back, but until that was done the one spot of light furnished by the bevy was a knot of white violets which one of them wore at the breast, and would not have covered for all the world. They chattered and laughed among themselves, these fine, adventurous and calm-eyed ladies; watched the arrivals and quizzed them, saw that Lord Rodono was uncomfortable, and spared him nothing. Mrs. Western vowed she would wave her handkerchief to the first man who named the Princess of Wales; and presently Vernour was mentioned and provoked curiosity. Everybody knew him and his tale; Hermia was begged to point him out. He was to speak? Then he would be on the platform and they could all see him. Was he really like the man in that horrible print? If so, he must be handsome, Lady Ogmore thought. Hermia, very composed outwardly, took all this with great

simplicity. As for Lord Rodono, he prepared himself
for the worst. Here he was with six handsome and fear-
less ladies on his hands, and an almost certain rumpus.
He had seen, but said nothing of certain Government
men dotted about the hall—one of whom he knew was in
receipt of pay. It was Hermia herself who saw and
called attention to Mr. Aloysius Banks, whose checked
muffler up to his chin made him a conspicuous object.
Meantime, the room was filling fast.

The leaders were on the hustings, they led in the body
of the hall, a tense and fervent assembly. Rodono, who
knew men, saw that there was hardly anybody present
who did not in his own way show himself braced for a
tussle. There was much variety: it was what you would
call a representative gathering. Blue-coated, nankeen-
breeched, prosperous traders leaned both hands solidly
upon their walking-sticks, and chatted after their way—
a few words snapped out at a time, a whisper behind the
hand, received with a nod. Sharp-faced men in black
smalls, with neat black legs and neater shoes, proved
brisker; they were full of jokes and of relish for jokes:
lawyers from the Hall, attorneys from Abingdon
Street were these. They exchanged snuff-boxes, capped
each other's puns, passed them on with nudges, and
knew everybody worth knowing. Watermen filled a
double row, red-faced and observant. It was one of
them who called for three cheers for the ladies when our
friends appeared, and led them, with one cheer more for

the handsomest. Behind them, closer packed, was a rougher sort—frieze-coated or long-waistcoated men in woollen stockings and highlows, who all kept heavy sticks between their knees, and had lowering brows and dogs' restless eyes. These were of the famous Westminster pack—chairmen, hackney-coachmen, stable hands, potmen, tinkers, costers, night-porters. They could be trusted to do anything, from chairing a candidate to breaking a Minister's windows, as they might be moved. They had many names: had been "Wilkes and Liberty men," "Fox's men," and now they were Burdett's men and Ranald's. One might be sorry for the Government spy whose head came within range of their blackthorns.

Hermia saw Vernour come in presently and make a way to the middle of the hall. He had a fine, leisurely way of pushing through a crowd, kept his head high and his shoulders very square, and leaned a little forward so that his weight might tell. She saw him the moment he entered, and hardly took her eyes off him again, but could not be sure whether he had discovered her presence or not. One of the strongest attractions he had for her was his seeming power of fitting her into a scheme of many things which all seemed equally important; so that she could never say that she was more to him than other interests. She was certain just now, for instance, that had she stood immediately before him and said, "I am here," he would have greeted her with ceremony, asked how she did, and have turned then to the real business of his evening. And the odd thing is that she loved him the better and admired him the more for this shared throne which he accorded her.

He stood easily in his place, taking off his scarf and caped coat, and nodded here and there to an acquaintance. With one or two he shook hands, but only when the salutation was thrust upon him; he never volunteered it. She saw a little black-browed man lean over from the lawyer's row and hold his hand out, and that Vernour added an inclination of the head as he took it. With others he was less concerned. The frieze coats had thumped with their sticks when he passed them, and Mr. Aloysius Banks stood up to have a good look at him. He was certainly considered at the Crown and Anchor.

Captain Ranald, who had received a storm of cheering on his entry, came off the hustings to speak to Vernour. The young man rose at his approach, bowed, and stood deferentially, listening to what was told him. He plainly demurred to some part of his instructions, and argued the difficulty with a calm persistence which got him his way. She who watched him so keenly was struck by the contrast between this pair, and, as you may guess, gave him the honours. The peer's son was all fire and vivacity, full of action of the hands and play of feature; the other held himself in reserve, and was stiff. When he spoke, he used no gestures. He seemed to be bending to an inferior; and she did not fail to notice that he got his way. So it was with the speeches which followed: she could

criticise Ranald, and found plenty of fault with him.
He disappointed her, and the more so because she knew
of what stuff he was; she had hoped that he would be as
direct on the platform as he had been at the dinner-table;
that he would be trenchant, and deal his strokes with the
gallantry which he certainly possessed. She had to own
him stilted and ornate while he was handling what was
really to the point, and only himself when he came, as
Rodono said he was bound to come, to the Navy and the
supply of seamen. He was cogent, weighty, and impres-
sive; but he roused no more enthusiasm at the close than
he had at the beginning of his speech—and to do that is
to fail. The truth, I suspect, is that the two sorts of men
who are natural on a platform are the deeply modest
man, who dares be nothing less, and the deeply conceited
man who cares not to be anything more. Between these
two extremes are all the varieties of human capacity.
This gallant gentleman respected his hearers and his
cause and, without over-valuation, respected himself;
but he clung to the traditions of oratory as to a good
coat for Sundays. Probably he would as soon have appeared on the quarter-deck of his ship without uniform
as have addressed the Westminster electors in anything
short of the periods of Mr. Burke.

Mr. Wardle succeeded him, Mr. Gwillym Wardle, famous friend of Mrs. Clark, who had no rhetorical scruples, and hesitated not to talk of rotten boroughs, place-
men, royal pensioners, and the like. He it was who

earned the promised handkerchief, for he spoke with
faltering voice of the Princess of Wales, as of a lady
"as beautiful as she was unhappy, and as unhappy as she
was royal," and raised a roar of agreement. Mr. Wardle, in fact, succeeded in what he had intended. He made
the auditory mischievous, when he gave them an inkling
of their power. "Ay, gentlemen," he cried, "shout for
that poor lady! And I would that the thunder of your
resentment could be heard across the way, and further
yet—across the park, gentlemen—as one of these days
it will be heard. And then, gentlemen, and then—God
help 'em!" None of this was very wise talk; but it was
exciting enough. By the time Vernour rose for his turn
it was plain that mischief was afloat.

He stood up in his place and held his head high; and
the gesture contributed not a little to an effect which to
one at least of his audience was overwhelming. It is not
often that one's preconception of character is borne out
by evidence so various as outward bearing and audible
speech may be. But Vernour seemed—proved himself—
to Miss Chambre to be all of a piece. She had built him
up from a moment's glimpse of his stiff head and hot
eyes; she had pictured him then as a man of destiny.
Nothing she had ever seen or heard of him had detracted
from that image. In his own shop—with the stuff of
his business about him—he had never compromised; in
the garden of her great house, it had been she who had
gone to him, and he who had waited for her to come; and

now, lastly, here, he spoke to the people as to her in the garden, in a manner assuredly innate. He was quiet, plain, succinct, with much in reserve. He had all the effect of meaning more than he said—which in oratory is the great effect; and he seemed to be in a position to threaten and to have certain knowledge which would make threats good. The thrilling undercurrent of personal triumph—she may have fancied that. . . . "I myself have felt the hand of tyranny on my neck, I myself have been pushed into the mire—but by the grace of God I am here to tell you so. If there is anything harder to bear than undeserved shame, I know not what it may be. It makes men mad, it makes them as wicked as their oppressors—and so the devil's work goes on. . . . What sustained me, lifted me up from the pit of degradation where I was soused is to you no matter, though to me it is all the world; but in kind the same solace is with that great man whom the tyrants of England think to have drowned. They have not drowned him, for you are holding up his head. They are here, listening to you and me. They dare us to save our hero's life . . . let them dare, but if they are wise they will stop in time. . . . " The audience was stirred with this piece of news; heads turned curiously; men looked at their neighbours; at the bottom of the hall somebody cried out, "Damn the spies!"

Vernour ended with a device which he may perhaps have got out of the Latin Syntax. "The people is enormously patient—we may pride ourselves on that—and it is slow.

We may pride ourselves on that, too—for this slowness and this patience are signs of enormous strength. Woe upon him who tempts the people! He will flog one man too many, imprison one man too long, and then——" He stopped in a dead silence; it was a fine rhetorical trick. His eyes shone, his head was high. He composed his voice to finish. "And then—all over, gentlemen, all over! That is revolution." He sat down, and there was a short silence before the storm began.

It began with a vague, indefinable stir, half shuffling of feet, half humming of voices all confused together; and then, no one knew exactly how, one man had another by the neck, three or four jumped up at once in different parts of the hall, crying "To hell with the spies! To hell with 'em!" The room seemed aswarm with white faces and tossing arms, and there was a continuous roar like that of the wind at night. Captain Ranald could be seen gesticulating from the hustings, but not heard; Mr. Wardle was buttoning his coat. Vernour, Miss Chambre watching him, stood with his arms folded, looking on what he had done—as if he had known as much before—his brows knitted, his chin sunk in his breast.

Rodono made her jump by his words in her ear. She had been far away. "We'll be out of this, I think, while we've time." The ladies rose and followed him down the stair; it would be necessary for them to enter the room and creep along by the wall to the door; but they were too late. The constables were in, using their staves, and the place was like the trenches with the bayonets at work. "Get back, get back," Rodono called over his shoulder, but Miss Chambre was already beside him, clear of the door; and almost immediately the lights were blown out. Rodono held the gallery-door, and his womankind clung together behind it. The fighting had settled down to serious work; the only sounds to be heard were grunts, groans, and deep breathing, with now and then the thwacks of a club, and a curse or cry of rage.

Whether Miss Chambre was frightened or not I cannot say for certain. All I know is that she leaned with her back to the wall, in complete darkness, and made no effort to gain the shelter of Lord Rodono's back. Her position was not without danger, for fighting or scuffling was going on so close to her that at times her cloak was swept forward or backward, and she might very well have been drawn into the thick of it; her foot was trodden; at any moment she could have become involved. How long she could have remained safely there, how long she did remain, neither she knew, nor do I; but she heard herself called, distinctly, by name—out of the dark, as before when she had stood waiting on the balcony—out of the dark, "Hermia—Hermia Mary," and she answered, "I am here," and held out her hands. They were caught, and by them she was drawn from her place; her form was gained, she was enclosed in a strong clasp, she was caught up against a strong breast. "My love, my love, Hermia!" Strong breath fanned her face, her lips were

possessed—and for a crowning moment she lost consciousness.

"Come, I will take you out of this," Vernour said, and
she knew that he could prove his words. Held closely by
his arm about her waist, she was half lifted, half led into
the air. It was a dark, warm and wet spring night; a
hot wind coming in squalls, scudding rain. The cobbles
gleamed under the flicker of lamps which swung and
tossed as the gust caught them. In the crowd about the
door, and in the semi-darkness of the night, his arm still
held her closely; but as they got free of people he let
her go, and they walked together in silence, she, at least,
very incapable of speech.

When he spoke, it was in his ordinary, carefully-con-
tained tone. "You are hurt? You are frightened?
That's not possible."

"No, no—not frightened." For her life she could not
have said more. Nothing in the world frightened her but
himself. He praised her courage.

"I was a fool to say what I knew could not be true.
Nothing could frighten you."

"No," she said—"nothing now."

He looked at her. "Why did you sigh?"

"Because you praise me. Because I am happy."

He threw his head up and laughed. "The good reason! The best! Come, I will escort you to your door.
You are in Clarges Street?"

"Yes—but how did you——?"

"It is my business to know everything about you. You have to be served wherever you may be. You have given me leave to do that."

"Am I to have my flowers—still? Now?"

"Surely," he said. "You are to have them till I die."

She thought this a wonderful thing—and told him so. What she did not add—perhaps she did not realise it yet—was that she wanted no more flowers. They, which had meant so much, now meant little; but she opened her cloak and showed him. "See," she said, "my badge."

"I saw it long ago. I gloried in you for that. Will you take my arm?" She put her hand lightly upon it, and they went on together, so.

They walked slowly—there was every reason not to hurry; they talked little, and she found out that her own class talks too much. There was no awkwardness in silence; it seemed to her, still trembling from his embrace, still conscious of her kissed lips, that there could never have been a day when she had not been in love with Vernour. If love was new to her, so was he. He was outside all her experience; she had known men strong, but not in this way. They expressed it by speech, he by refraining from speech. If they loved her, they told her so; but she believed the more in this man's love the less he said of it. So she walked in miracle, in touch with a miraculous being, with a heart too full even for wonder. She would have walked into the Thames had he chosen it, or up to a cannon's mouth. She discussed nothing, unless he opened upon the subject—neither plans, nor the past; but she did ask him how he had found her, and thrilled at his answer: "I knew where you were at every moment of the evening. I saw you come down to the door."

"But you did not look at me; you never did."

"Did I not?" He laughed. "I am always looking at you. I am looking at you now. I am loving you now. I will tell you what I think."

"Tell me, please."

"I think that after to-night I must see you always."

"Yes." He said no more, and she could not. It seemed that she must be for ever kept upon the edge of bliss.

She took no thought for the morrow, since he, the master of her mind, proposed to her none. She did not ask him what she was to say to her grandmother; that lady did not enter her head. She walked by his side—a girl in the spring—utterly contented; and it was not until they were near the door of the house in Clarges Street that she remembered her needs. Her needs? The single need, which was to know when she could see him again. But then, as he made no proposals, it was necessary to stop him.

"Oh," she said, "we are here!"

"Yes, we must go our ways now."

"Will you come no further?"

"I shall take you to the door. It is close by us now."

Her hand pressed his arm—he stooped to her. "My love," he said, "my love!"

"I am to lose you now—it is hard. When will you come again?"

He thought for a moment. "It is very needful to see you soon. Something must be done—settled. I will come into the garden to-morrow night at ten—if you—if it will be possible."

"Possible! Oh, yes. I will be there."

He told her, "It must be for the last time. This cannot go on—on this footing. Now, good-bye. No, no—I must not——"

She held out her hand to him without a word, and he kissed it. He was plainly seen to kiss it by Captain Ranald and Lord Rodono, who were on the doorstep of the house in Clarges Street. How much more these gentlemen had collected it would not be easy to guess.

"Thank God she's safe, at least," said Ranald, and ran down to meet her. "Good Lord, Miss Chambre—and thank the good Lord! We have had half London hunting for you. Rodono and I have just got in—we've been everywhere."

"Thank you, Captain Ranald—I was perfectly safe all the time. I found a friend, or rather he found me: Mr. Vernour."

"Yes," said Ranald, very slowly—"yes, I believe that you are safe with Vernour."

Rodono held the door open for her, anxious ladies were

in the hall. "Is she——? Have you——? Oh, my dearest, my dearest child!" She was enfolded, kissed, and made much of. But Lord Rodono's chilly eyes looked through her into the wall beyond, seeing nothing. They were like the eyes of a fish, had never been colder.

"Thank you, Lord Rodono, for hunting me," she said, as she ran into the arms of Mrs. Western.

"Tom," said Ranald, as he buttoned his great-coat, "I'll take you with me to Brooks's, I think. It'll do you good." So they went together.

CHAPTER XXIX

ORDEAL BY BATTLE

LORD RODONO, at Brooks's with his friend, had been clear as to what he intended to do, so clear and clear in such a way that Ranald could hardly intervene. After all, it was true that Tom was in love; and a man in love may do more than a man out of it. Ranald, when he was pressed, could not admit that he was in love with the lady. He was neutral, he said, not greatly caring whether she married Vernour or not, so long as she married the man of her heart. "I'm not at all in love with her," he said, "but I like her well enough to hope that her marriage will be made in heaven, and not in Caryll House. I like her very much indeed; I admire her spirit and good sense; I think she's as handsome a young woman as London contains. I think myself a fool that I am not over head and ears in love—but there I stop. The fact is, I'm not a romantic man, I'm not a philandering man. No offence to you, though."

Lord Rodono, very stiff and staring, consumed brandy and water steadily, stopping only to glare at the fire, strengthen the fold of his arms and tap his foot on the carpet. "This is more than scandalous, upon my heart and conscience. I'm more shocked than I can say. She!

that peerless, that splendid—Dick Chambre's girl—fine
descent on both sides—Fitzgerald blood, Caryll, Botetort—she! and a damned, mouthing Radical butcher!
Oh, God, Ranald—it makes Othello of me."

"Don't let it make Iago, my friend," said Ranald; "you
overdo that battening business—which is sickly work for
a man of your parts. The fellow's not a butcher any
more, but as good as you or I. For that matter, I believe
him to be a good deal better." He looked down upon the
incensed man rigid in his chair. "I think you may make
mischief, Tom—I do, indeed. I know the man, and you
don't. I tell you again, he's a fine fellow—a man of
strength. Could you or I have spoken as he did? Answer for yourself. I know very well that I could not.
In what makes a man essentially a gentleman he's well
found. I'll go bail for him, Vernour would never stoop
to a blackguardly thing."

Lord Rodono glared at him. "Has he not, by heaven!
Has he not repaid her finely for her generosity? Answer me that."

Ranald thought for a moment before he took up the
challenge. He plunged his hands deep in his breeches
pockets. "Upon my honour," he said, "I think she'll
make him a good wife." Up jumped Rodono, breathing short. "Do you care to laugh at me, Ranald?"

"No, I do not. I mean what I say. I believe in her
more than you do, after all, it seems to me; for I'm dead
certain that she'd never let a man touch her unless she

liked him, nor would like a man unless he were a fine one. I could say no more for my sister—and it ought to come from you rather than me. I confess I don't understand your sort of love, Rodono. You say, I adore this lady, I believe her to be all that is excellent in women —on condition that she loves me. The moment she chooses for somebody else, you cease to believe in her, but go on loving. My good friend, you'll forgive me for saying that that is more like craving than loving."

Lord Rodono regarded him coldly, and then turned on his heel. "I wish you good-night, Ranald," he said over his shoulder as he went. It's ill reasoning with an angry man. Ranald let him go.

The meeting took place in the garden, at the appointed hour. Her ladyship had dined abroad, and Hermia was to be escorted to join her at eleven, then to be taken to a party at Lady Crowland's. Dining alone—for Harriet was away—she had fidgeted herself into a fever for the keeping of her tryst; and this made her very shy and very humble. Her lover's conduct drove her bashfulness out of her. He was grave and unapproachable. "My love," he said, "I am greatly to blame for this underhand way in which I lead you. I beg your pardon; there shall be no more."

Frightened out of her wits, she begged him to explain himself. Did he—could he mean——? Oh, no, no, he could not mean—— She was timid, but with all the world at stake she drew near and touched him on the arm. He gave a short cry, and took her. She gave him her lips, which he had made his already. He strained her to his breast. Quite out of herself, she lay weeping in his arms.

He mastered his transport, with another cry which sounded as if he were angry, and would have put her away; but now she would not go. The fountain of her heart was unsealed now; her lips had been conquered, her waist made prisoner. Hugging her chains, she must give him all—nay, she could not be denied that bliss. So it was, "Hold me, oh my love, kiss me, touch me. Let me know myself yours." For a moment he yielded to her desire, but only for a moment. Resolutely then he put her from him and told her that they must meet no more until they could meet the world. Even she acknowledged the difficulty there, and had to own that she didn't know how to go to work. He said, with his head high, that he should wait upon her ladyship in the morning, and then she had to tell him how far out of the question that was. "They will insult you, and I couldn't bear that."

"Better me than you, my dear," said he; but she denied it.

"I know granny very well. She will not hurt me at all; she will be very cold; she will send me to my room and keep me there—I shall stop in it—as I did before when— I saw you for the first—no, for the second time. In the end she will either forget me, and I shall walk out, or she will open the door for me herself and tell me to do as

I please. You know, David, that I am of age. But I must tell you one thing—if you take me, you will take a beggar. I have a little money now—more since my darling brother died—but it all goes if I don't marry granny's choice."

"My love," he said, "I want none of your money. I am well enough in money—but I shall need all your forbearance. You know me as I am—you have seen me as I must be——" His broken voice made her cry; she could have kneeled to him. She came to him, took his hand, lifted it and kissed it. "My King David—my king of men." He put his arm about her very gently, and, stooping, kissed her lips. "You will make me a king yet, my love. I will be—I can be whatever you choose to have me. Now leave me, my soul—I will see your grandmother in the morning—and you again when I have earned you."

This was so serious that she had at all costs to stop it, by telling him that she intended to have the story out to-night. "Come, if it seems good to you, David, to-morrow. I assure you that you will do me harm if you do. I can bear that—I can bear anything you bid me; but you will hurt me very much—I must tell you that." In the end, he gave in. He would not come until he was sent for; he promised her.

Then he was all for going, with as little ceremony as might be—and she all for keeping him by her. All the witchery of woman was now at her command—and when she couldn't move him, she threw herself upon him, sobbing and imploring—"Once, David—please, once! Oh, what shall I do! What shall I do!"

He put his hands upon her shoulders and gently held her away. "My dear, you mustn't cry, you mustn't, indeed. No, no—I'm very nearly lost—but now I'll never give in. Hermia, listen to me now. I'm strong again, thank the Lord. I love you so well that I dare not touch you until we have told our tale to the world. You won't ask me—you will never ask me. Oh, I know you—you will never ask me. If you love me now, you will go in."

She stopped her crying at once, and of her own accord stepped back out of his reach. "Yes, I will obey you. I beg your pardon. Good-night." She turned and went to the house without looking behind her.

Vernour watched her as far as the light could discover her to him, and waited for the door to close upon her before he left the garden. Then he went to the gap in the wall—Lady Hermione's gap, not yet repaired—and jumped for it, pulled himself up, and dropped into the park, almost at the feet of a tall gentleman, waiting there, evidently for him—a gentleman in a cocked hat and cloak, distinguishable by a white muffler round his neck. It was so obvious, his awaiting, that Vernour waited also.

The stranger had a harsh and stern voice. "A word with you—you who are in and out like a thief."

"Who are you that speak so to me?"

He was answered, "One with a right. My name is Turnbull. They call me Lord Rodono."

Vernour inclined his head ever so slightly. "I have heard of your lordship. For the sake of what I have heard, I will tell you this. The last thief in and out of here was Colonel Chambre, and I have the word of his daughter for it."

This was a palpable hit. Lord Rodono had no immediate reply. When he found one, he felt that it was lame.

"The cases are not on a level, Vernour. Colonel Chambre was my friend, and a gentleman. He was in all respects her ladyship's equal. You have no such pretensions, I understand."

"I have no pretensions at all, my lord, save those which I can claim from having found favour in Miss Chambre's eyes."

"We will leave names out, if you please. I have used none, and will use none but my own and yours. I deny your right to anything but chastisement."

"Chastisement, my lord!" said Vernour quickly. "Chastisement from——?"

"From me, sir."

"What right have you to chastise me?"

"The right which you have to defend yourself. I am a friend and frequenter of this house. It is my business to defend any in it who have no other defenders."

Vernour said, "There are other, more natural defenders," and gave his opponent an advantage.

"The natural defenders are dead, sir," said Rodono; "as you ought—as you seem to have known." Then Vernour recovered his ground.

"I ought to have remembered that, my lord. You are right there. But they being dead, I beg leave to tell your lordship that I am now the natural defender of——"

"Damn you! be silent."

"I was silent," said Vernour, "until your lordship interrupted me." Lord Rodono bit his lip.

"Vernour," he said then, "this is to stop. In my opinion, you have betrayed the greatest honour ever paid to a man of your station; you have repaid generosity by the basest ingratitude. You have given treachery for confidence; you are a cheat and a thief."

"I cannot take those words from you, Lord Rodono," said Vernour very quietly, "and I must ask you to withdraw them."

"On the contrary," said Rodono, "I shall repeat them. You are a traitor, a cheat, and a thief."

"My lord," Vernour said, "you must fight me for that."

"I fight with gentlemen, sir. Not with butchers."

"Don't let my trade stand in your way, my lord. It should not, for it was your own."

His lordship started. "You are impudent, my man, as well as a rogue, I see."

"Sir," said Vernour, "you were a soldier, I've been told.

What difference there may be between us seems to be to my credit. I made sheep bleed, you made men bleed. I carved joints—you carved limbs. You butchered your own kind, you slew men. I made men live. Now, my lord."

"Damn him, he's right there," said Lord Rodono to himself.

"My lord," said Vernour, "you force me to make a boast of my trade—though it is no longer mine—because you disparage me upon grounds not worthy of your occupation. If you had told me I was a vile fellow— a coward, a glutton, a beast, it would have been better, for you might have believed it upon some report. But you know I am none of those, and you choose to say that my rank is not of your own, therefore you will not fight me. I think that you should leave that plea to persons who have no other defence. I am as honest as yourself, my lord, and no readier with my hands, I dare swear. Why, sir, you protect yourself in the manner of my Lord Morfa, who, having staked my horse and damned me for a tradesman, cried out, in his own forecourt, that he dared such a blackguard lay hands on a lord. I am no more bound to listen to you with such a plea in your mouth than I was to listen to him. If I am to believe you a man of the sort, and go from you now, you will call me a coward, and say that I shirked an encounter. If I am to credit your behaviour of this occasion, such blame from you will be better than your praise. I wish you good-night." He turned and walked a few steps of his way home; but Lord Rodono followed him.

"Vernour," he said, "I'll fight you if you please."

"Where?" says Vernour.

"Why, we'll go in the park, I think," said his lordship. "We'll be snug enough there."

"Come along, my lord," the other replied. So they went.

Across the Knightsbridge Road, with its scattered edging of little white villas in their gardens, lay Hyde Park, behind a low fence of post and rail. Save for a transient cry now and then from some outcast wandering there, the place seemed a desert. In the midst of a grove of elms these two young men stripped to the shirt and fought, but before they began, Vernour said, "Bear me witness, my lord, that I do this against my will. But so it is that you have put more scorn upon me than I can bear, honoured as I have been of late, glorified as I am now. For this reason I must fight with you—but I'd ask a favour of your lordship, to shake hands before we begin."

"I won't refuse that," said the young lord. They shook hands and faced each other.

They were much of a height, but in girth the butcher was the finer man, and in length of reach, in wind and agility unquestionably the finer. Lord Rodono had science—every man had in that day; this was not the

first time he had stripped for battle; Vernour had, perhaps, less—but he had the cooler temper.

They fought three rounds, during the first of which
Rodono did all the work he was able, and Vernour had
as much as he could do to stop him without savagery.
It may have lasted four or five minutes, and need not
have taken two. Rodono's wind—none too good—failed
him, and in the end he fell. The second was shorter.
Rodono made a rush, and was stopped; he made another
in which he closed; a brief mill finished him, and again he
fell. In the third round Vernour, who was perfectly
fresh, forced the fighting—honestly wishing to be merci-
ful—beat down his man's guard and caught him under
the chin with his left. Lord Rodono fell once more, and
lay still.

"Are you hurt, my lord? Are you hurt?" Vernour
was kneeling by him now, hovering and anxious. Rodono
presently sat up. "No, no, not at all. You've done
your business very well. Help me up, will you?" He
did; the two shook hands.

"Now I'll tell you, Vernour," said Rodono, "that I am
a suitor for the hand of the lady to whom you pretend."
Vernour said nothing; so he went on. "That gives me
no right to use words to you which you properly resented
—and punished; but I am not able to agree with you in
the suitability of the arrangement you propose. I am
quite sincere in saying that I shall oppose this match
tooth and nail, simply on this ground, that it will end in

misery, and a kind of life which no lady, brought up as this lady has been, ought to be called upon to face. What influence I have will be used against you, and you will wrong me if you think I do it for my own prospects. You will wrong me, I say."

"I will never wrong your lordship," said Vernour quickly. "I believe what you tell me. Now, let me tell your lordship this. That lady has given me proof undeniable that I have won her heart. She has told me that I did that without speaking with her more than once, or seeing her more than thrice. I admit that I courted her, after she had paid me great honour, by a way of my own. But I never hoped to win her, and I should have continued my courtship until she asked me to stop, whether she was to be lost or won. Courtship! It was not that in the beginning—it was like the homage you pay to your king! It was not until I saw that she wore my flowers——"

"What!" cried Rodono, staring. "It was you—those white violets! By God, man, you're a poet, I see."

"You flatter me, my lord," said Vernour. "I'm no poet. But I had to offer the best thing I could find to the noblest being I had ever dreamed of. She'll have them till I die."

"I see that I've been floored by a proper man," said Lord Rodono. "I'll think this out. Good-night." They shook hands and parted. So much for ancient chivalry, not dead, the reader perceives, in 1810.

Men fight for women, women for their souls. Hermia, in a tremble of excitement, waited for her grandmother outside the house in Bruton Street, where her ladyship had dined, knowing full well that her battle was to come. Her suspense had to endure, as best it might, through an hour or more of chatter and gallantry at Crowland House—Tom Moore's effervescence, Sidney Smith's acidity, Mr. Rogers's astringency, and Mr. Greville's asperity. When they were in the great chariot, rumbling home through the empty Kensington roads, she plunged into her subject headlong. She spoke too fast, because her breath failed her. She had learned her opening by heart, but got it wrongly.

"I think it right to tell you, grandmamma, that I have been asked—that for some time past I have been thinking —great attentions have been paid me by a gentleman— and I have—I have allowed——"

"Your cousin, George Coigne, I suppose you mean," said her ladyship; but Hermia said that it was not. "I know that you had the thought in your head that George and I might be married; but as you said nothing to me about it, I didn't like to tell you that it was out of the question."

"Oh, indeed," said Lady Morfa, in her ordinary voice. Those who suppose that she would alter that by a quarter-tone to answer, say, the Last Trumpet, do not know yet the Queen Mother of the Carylls. It was dark in the carriage, and not possible to see the stiffening old head, or the blinking of the fierce old eyes. "Oh, indeed! Then, pray, who is this gentleman?"

"It is a gentleman whom I have met but two or three times, though I know a great deal of him—otherwise, and esteem all that I know. For nearly a year he has sent me flowers—you may have seen them."

"No, my dear," said Lady Morfa, "I assure you that this is the first I have heard of it, though, no doubt, I am the only person in the house who is ignorant."

"I fancy that you are," said Miss Chambre. "I have worn them daily or nightly ever since they began to come. White violets."

"Ah, yes," said Lady Morfa, "now I think I have noticed them. Please to go on."

"The gift, the continuance of it, the nature of it—and other things about it—touched me greatly. I thought of it often; and so, when the giver of it spoke to me, I consented to hear him—and I must consider myself engaged. Of course, I know very well——"

"What I suppose you know by this time, though I have no proof of it, is this gentleman's name?"

"Grandmamma, that's not quite fair, because, if you remember, I told you that I knew a great deal about him. I know it perfectly well, and so do you—but you won't like it at all, I'm afraid. I must tell you first that I have thought very seriously about it—it is very strange, but I think I have been—interested in him for a long, long time. And now I have passed him my word, and can never give him up. He is Mr. David Vernour."

Lady Morfa started. "You are mad," she said.

"No, no, I can't allow that. I love him dearly."

Lady Morfa certainly shivered—but it was her every-day voice which said, "I am much obliged to you for this news." And then she said nothing more. Hermia was on the point to speak more than once—but each time checked herself. Of what use to speak? She knew what was to be done to her.

As the carriage entered the gates, Lady Morfa did speak. She said, "Will you have the goodness to remain in your room to-morrow until I see you? I shall have something to say."

"Yes, granny, certainly."

She said also, "Good-night, granny," as she went up-stairs, but got no reply.

Lady Morfa had a command for her maid. "I wish to speak to Moth here before she goes to bed; and to-mor-row morning let Miss Moon see me so soon as she leaves her room."

Mrs. Moth came fluttering in to find her ladyship bolt upright in her chair before the fire.

"Moth," said the Queen Mother, "you will leave this house to-morrow morning. The steward will have your wages ready for you. You will get no character from me but a true one; and, therefore, I advise you not to apply for it."

"Very good, my lady," faltered Mrs. Moth, curtseyed, and withdrew.

To Harriet Moon the same fate was decreed. "You will leave this house by midday. You will have no communication with any person here except Mr. Hanse, who will pay you what is due."

"Yes, my lady," the brown-eyed girl whispered, curtseyed, and withdrew. But it is to be stated of her that a communication was made—not with Mr. Hanse.

CHAPTER XXX

WHICH ATTACKS IN FLANK

MRS. GEORGE FOX, that bosom friend of Hermia's, had come post-haste to town, anxious to know the worst. She arrived two or three days only after the girl's imprisonment, and saw Lady Morfa. A charming, motherly, kind-eyed woman, soft and round and purring, was Mrs. George Fox.

"Oh, Lady Morfa, I have had such an uncomfortable letter from Hermy that I haven't been able to rest for worrying about it. Pray, pray, tell me what it means."

"It means," said Lady Morfa, "that she proposes to disgrace my name."

"Oh, but that is terrible—that is not possible!"

"It is, unfortunately, very possible, and it would be terrible if she were to do it. But she will not."

Mrs. Fox was nearly speechless, but luckily she was curious.

"I feared—when I received her letter—the letter, I assure you, of one—I hardly know—of one fixed in purpose—of one under a terrible fate! Lady Morfa, who is this man? She mentioned no name—she even said that she was not sure——"

"I can imagine that she would not care to mention it.

It is a tradesman—a tradesman's son. He is a Radical—
I don't give that as an excuse, far from it."

"A Radical—ah!" It was a good deal of excuse to
Mrs. Fox. "Hermy's ideas, you know, Lady Morfa!
Well, it is just what poor Lord Edward would have done
—*just!*"

"To my mind," said her ladyship, "it is very much
what Lord Edward *did* do—if he didn't do worse—but I
can hardly enter into such matters with you."

"No," said the anxious lady, not knowing what other
reply was expected of her.

"You can suppose," continued her ladyship, "that this
intelligence was unwelcome. I cannot say that it was unexpected. Arrangements had been made for an alliance
eminently suitable to my granddaughter's position and
prospects. Sir George Coigne, my nephew—everything
that one could wish—a really fine property—a powerful
county influence—but I need not fatigue you with particulars."

"Pray spare yourself, dear Lady Morfa."

"I have. taken proper steps to protect this unfortunate
girl against herself and her seducers——"

"Oh, pray, pray——!" cried Mrs. Fox, but Lady
Morfa was not to be prayed.

"I say her seducers, for I think there were more than
one. I have dismissed her waiting-woman and a young
person who had stood for some years in a confidential
capacity to me personally, but with whom, I am sorry

to say, Hermia had chosen to become unduly intimate. Nothing could really have been expected of such an intimacy but what has happened. That person left my house the day after I had been told what was going on. I think that she regretted the return she had made me for a good deal of kindness, one way with another. What I propose to do now is to apply to the Lord Chancellor to have the girl made a ward of court."

"Very wisely, no doubt," murmured Mrs. Fox—and then with clasped hands and a tear in the voice she urged, "Oh, Lady Morfa, may I—might I—see her? I love her so dearly—we are such old friends."

"Really, I will ask you not to hope for that at present," said her ladyship. "No good could be expected—at present—from any such kindness as I am sure you meditate. I have not yet seen her myself. Seclusion, thought (I hope), repentance——"

"Prayer," the other lady suggested, at random.

"Prayer? Ah, no doubt—very right and proper," said her ladyship loftily—but she didn't like it. Any suggestion that application could be addressed elsewhere than to herself offended her a good deal.

That really closed the discussion. Mrs. Fox took her leave, with the statement that she should remain in town for some few weeks—at the house of her cousin, Lord Nahir—a respectable, though Irish viscount.

A particular bitterness of Lady Morfa's had not been

mentioned by her, and could never have been mentioned
by her to any Mrs. Fox. It is doubtful whether a Marquis
of Badlesmere—a Botetort and her brother—or an Honourable Venerable—an Archdeacon and a Caryll—could
have been told a secret so mortifying. It was that both
her son and nephew—the head of the Carylls and Sir
George Coigne—had shown much more concern over the
dismissal of Miss Harriet Moon than for Hermia Mary's
desperate disgrace. Lord Morfa had turned very white
when he heard it. At the Vernour story he had chuckled
—"What a go!" he had said. "Hope that stilted beast
Sandgate will feel happy. Nastyish for Tom—eh,
ma'am? By Gad, I must let Prinny know about
this. That man Vernour—did you hear, ma'am?—he's
a champion, by Gad! He is, though. He had a battle
on Stockbridge Down with Exeter Jack, and knocked
him out in three rounds! No wonder Beauty got his
nose dabbed! My word, though—Hermy, eh? Well,
that beats the cocks—by Gad, it does——" And more
to the same elementary effect.

But when his mother told him of condign punishment
upon the sly Moon, he turned sick white. "You've done
that! You've sent her packing! Oh, I don't—I can't
——!" Then, after a pause, "I tell you, ma'am, you've
made mischief. You'd no business to interfere."

"Interfere, Roderick!"

"Well—what I mean is—you've made mischief—dam-
nable mischief! No, no—I can't hear you—I can't talk

about Miss Moon to you. Look here, ma'am—that was
an infernal shame! She was innocent as a babe unborn
—and you know that very well. You never liked her—
you know you didn't; and she was afraid of you, and
showed it, and you bullied her. Poor little girl—poor
little Harriet! I tell you what it is, ma'am, I'm upset—
I'm downright ill at such infern—at such injustice.
Tyranny, I call that—rank tyranny!"

"Roderick, Roderick—my son! what are you saying to
me?"

"I'm telling you what I think of what you've chosen to
do. Wreak your vengeance on the family, ma'am, if
you please. You've shocked me—I wouldn't have had
such a thing done in my house for ten thousand pound
—I wish you joy of your work, Lady Morfa—and good-
morning to you." He had gone out of the room—she
heard him shouting for his man—and she had not been
able to move. His valet came anxiously to her. "His
lordship's compliments, my lady, and he wishes for the
keys of the corridor." Positively so; and she had sent
them. He must have gone to see Hermia—and she let
him go. He had left the house—his trunks (a round
dozen of them) followed with his secretary in a hackney-
coach, his valet on the box—and she not able to move;
and she had seen no more of him. This made her very
ill; but Sir George's tears—yes, his round eyes had
brimmed over, the man—a Botetort and a baronet—

had fairly blubbered over the wrongs of a Moon—this, very fortunately, strengthened her. She found herself again, as they say; and the close imprisonment of Hermia Mary went on.

The child's friends, meantime, were active, for the story was all about the town. Tom Creevy was heard whispering and chuckling about it to Mr. Sheridan at Brooks's; but he stopped when Lord Sandgate came into the room. "Sandgate's been hit"—he told his friend— "badly hit, he's been. I happen to know." What was there Tom Creevy did not happen to know? Mighty little, I suspect.

It was Mrs. Fox who took the tale to Lady Grizel— to whom her brother Rodono had vouchsafed nothing of it; but for all that Lady Grizel had had it, in a letter from the disgraced girl herself—a letter written that first night of her incarceration, and actually in Moth's pocket at the moment of her dismissal; and Moth had related all that the letter did not. Hermia's letter had been very short:

"DEAREST GRIZEL: I must tell you how proud and happy I am to have won the love and respect of Mr. Vernour. I have been engaged to him for ten days, and every moment since then has but added to the honour he has done me. I hope I shall make him a good and obedient wife. I shall try my hardest, and know he will be very patient. Granny is *horrified*—but that makes no difference. With fondest love,

"Ever your HERMY.

"P.S.—If you think that my news would interest dear Lord Drem and your brother, will you tell them how proud I am?"

That was a difficult letter to deal with. Old Lord Drem said that he didn't understand it; such things had not been done in his time—at least, he could only recollect one case—that of Sophia Weyburn who had married a Glasgow notary—and there had been cogent reasons for that. All he could say was that it pointed to a very exceptional young man, or a very exceptional young lady. Lord Rodono said nothing, but his sister saw the chill settle on his blue eyes. As for herself, her feelings may perhaps be gathered from her reply—which never reached its address:

"DEAREST: I can hardly answer your beautiful letter—for beautiful it is, whatever one may think of its news. My dear, what am I to say about that? All I can urge upon you is reflection, serious and ample reflection. I know your *ideas*, how truly *democratic* you are, and perhaps I ought to be able to follow you, and indeed in *opinion* I do—but in *judgment*, dearest love, I cannot, at present. How much can you, how little do you not, know of Mr. V.? Pray think of this, and do nothing precipitate. Dear papa was very kind. You know the Drum-Major's way! I have told Tom—I thought it kinder. He said nothing—but he was very much moved. At any rate, you have *three friends* in this house—and always will have. Count upon us, my love, I implore you. I shall try to prevail upon Lady M. to let me see you for a minute—or even to speak with you through the *key-hole!* Darling Hermy, my heart is *wae* for you.

"GRIZEL."

This letter was not opened, but was left with others addressed to the prisoner on her ladyship's escritoire.

Upon that same escritoire, upon a day to be shortly named, lay two other letters in Lady Morfa's hand, sealed with the Caryll seal, one addressed to Thomas Vernour—Brook Street—and the other to the Marquis of Badlesmere, K.G., of which letter I shall not speak further than to say that it requested that nobleman to invoke the powers of Lord Eldon in her favour. The letter to Vernour the elder ran thus:

"The Countess of Morfa has to inform T. Vernour that his visits to Caryll House for custom must instantly cease. Her ladyship believes that Vernour will understand the reason of this order, and has further to say that any appearance of either Thomas or David Vernour will be followed by an action for trespass. The Countess of Morfa cannot condescend to particulars of offences peculiarly abominable which have rendered summary measures necessary. Caryll House, April 30th, 1810."

Now for the reason why that letter was never sent.

On the morning of April 30th—Hermia having been imprisoned for some ten days—a Mr. Custance called at Caryll House and was introduced into Lady Morfa's room; a grave, elderly man, considerably bald, low-voiced, sententious, and a lawyer. He made a ceremonious bow at the door; he advanced, as it were, soft-footed to the middle of the room; bowed again, with his hat covering his heart. "Madam," he said, "my lady——" and then he came near to the table and made his final bow.

"Be seated, sir," said Lady Morfa, but with a wave of his hat he excused himself.

"My lady," he said, "I am my Lord Morfa's accredited agent in a matter of some consequence to his lordship and of some interest to yourself." Lady Morfa did not look at him.

"Lord Morfa's agents are familiar to me, by name, at least. I don't recollect that yours is one of them."

"My lady," said Mr. Custance, and produced his pocket-book, and drew from it a card, "here are my credentials —or some of them. The writing upon this card will be very familiar to your ladyship." The card bore the name of Mr. Oliver Custance, Doctors' Commons, and over that "Introduced upon my particular affairs. Morfa."

Lady Morfa moistened her lips as she put the card down. "I will listen to you, sir," she said, "but must beg you to be brief."

"Madam," said Mr. Custance, "I will be brief. I need not, I think, refer at any length to the circumstances—distressing as they must have been—under which my noble client felt it his duty——"

"No, sir," said her ladyship, "you need not. I beg that you will make no reference whatever to any matter which is not your immediate concern. I asked you to be brief, and you threaten to be lengthy. Have the goodness to inform me of your actual business here."

"My lady——" Mr. Custance was disturbed.

"Your business, sir, if you please."

"I will obey you, my lady. I have the honour to inform your ladyship that your son, my Lord Morfa, was married yesterday by special license to Miss Harriet Moon. Lord and Lady Morfa have repaired to Brighton for a short visit, but propose returning to town shortly—I think to a house in Curzon Street, but am not yet fully advised. My lady, I regret this abrupt——" There he stopped, because he observed that Lady Morfa's head was sunk and nodding helplessly to her breast. Dull purple suffused her cheeks, her breath came shuddering and thick. Mr. Custance crossed the room rapidly and pulled the bell. Assistance was not long in coming. Her ladyship was got to bed; and Hermia Mary left her prison to watch by her grandmother's side.

From that silent bedside, in the watches of the night, she wrote to Vernour:

"My grandmamma is very ill, and I must not leave her yet, though she has been cruel to you and to me. You have my heart, and can direct my will, but I know that you will ask nothing of me which I ought not to do. Write to me, and tell me that you trust me. Nothing can keep me from you when you call me. HERMIA MARY."

Next day she was in the arms of Mary Fox.

CHAPTER XXXI

WHICH MRS. GEORGE FOX UNDERSTANDS

LADY BARWISE was extremely surprised to find herself in any sort of agreement with a Mrs. George Fox. "The Chambre connection—but really a person of proper feeling. That most unhappy child—impossible that she should remain here for a moment. Dearest mamma is so sensitive—and they say that the Prince—so altogether I was thankful to get rid of her; and Mrs. Fox was perfectly reasonable, and very kind about it." Mrs. Fox had, in fact, jumped at a proposal which she would have hesitated herself to open. The culprit was given over to her; she had her safely now in her Brompton lodgings, where for a time she was seldom out of her arms.

After the first cooings and tear-minglings — with "There, then, my precious, you are safe with your Mary—cry your fill"—she had attempted gentle admonitions of that sort which any good woman, with howsoever fine an ardour she have embraced matrimony, always feels constrained to give. No wife, we may suppose, ever forgets the plunge into the dark which has preceded her happiness; and no girl ever believes in it. Therefore, so long as Mrs. Fox confined herself to platitude her doctrine was accepted with docility. Her friend was too young to deal with generalities, and accepted them as the insignia of matrons. But when the good lady was forced, by honest belief, to go further, when it became evident that she frankly deplored the betrothal, Miss Hermia became the amazon; and it was a fierce young face that lifted from Mary's bosom, and a pair of scornful eyes which made Mary's to quail.

"Unworthy! You call him unworthy!"

"His position, dearest. Think of his position—and yours!"

"Why should I think of what my mother gave no thought to? Would you have called my father unworthy?"

"Your father, my darling, was my own cousin."

"Well, everybody must be somebody's cousin, I suppose. If I am to be careful of your cousins, Mary, I do think you should remember Mr. Vernour's."

"Your father was undoubtedly a gentleman," said Mrs. Fox.

To which she replied, "And so is Mr. Vernour, without any kind of doubt."

"Not in the eyes of the world, Hermy."

The girl's own eyes grew dreamy, and her voice sounded tired. "The world! I had forgotten it. Where is the world? Inside the Caryll House gates, I believe—defended by Jacob Jacobs. Surely I came out of it when I came to you!" After which there was nothing immediately to be done—by the likes of Mrs. Fox—but to kiss her; and presently to take up the burden again.

There was, you see, the romantic side to this affair; and Mary Fox, a long and patient traveller in the Pays du Tendre, was allured into occasional peeps at her old haunts—whose whispering groves, whose rills and thickets still had power to charm. Having the case before her, put with an impassioned oratory which I shall not attempt to rehearse, she had to confess that conduct more irreproachably delicate than that of the violet-bearer could not be conceived. It partook of the marvellous, even; for how did a Brook Street tradesman—and of his trade of all trades in the world!—how did such a one conjure up white violets all the year round? Pass, as Hermia calmly passed, the nursery-gardener at Feltham—to what research it pointed! To what an instinct for the elegant! Yes, and to what nice passion! When she was told as a fact that her Hermy had fallen in love with a posy of flowers, she had, in her present mood, no difficulty in believing it. She could understand that, she could imagine it. There was Boccaccio's tale—Lisabetta fondling her pot of basil: yes, she could thrill at such a tale! But by so much as you heighten the lure of that, by so much the more must the truth revolt. When the mystery was unlocked, when the veiled lover stood before her as he was—what then? Here her young friend confounded her by a dazzling admission, for she simply said that she then knew she had been in love before—"be-

cause, Mary, I was so happy, and liked to think of him."
Yes, yes, indeed, that was the way of it—that was the
glorious estate. One "liked to think of him"! But if
one had been thinking of a violet-bearer, clothed in the
mossy fragrance of his tribute, shy and rare himself as
that in which he hid—and then—oh, heaven!—the white
flowers brushed aside, he stood up, garbed in his dreadful
uniform! What then, child?

"Then," said Hermia, "I remembered that I had liked
to think of him before."

"Before! Then you had—oh, my dearest!"

"I had seen him, of course, Mary. He was the very
first person I saw when I came to London." And thus it
gradually appeared to have been a case of love at first
sight—kindled by a chance spark—a vision of proud
eyes and a stiff head; blown upon by a visit to Brook
Street; set ablaze by subsequent meetings—ah me!
"Harriet told me long ago that I was interested in him
because I admired him," she said. "I was angry with
her and thought she had a common mind; but you see
that she was right. I didn't know it . . . but she was
perfectly right."

She was able to speak of Brook Street by-and-by—
almost to explain Brook Street. She had been praised
for courage, she said, and named Lord Sandgate; as a
matter of truth, she had been "dreadfully afraid. But it
had to be done, you see," she went on. "I couldn't help
doing it—I was drawn there—and now—and now I know

why." Democracy, indeed! Mary Fox began to know why, too.

Talking of that visit, she skirted the inner truth, or delayed her search for it. She said that her prevalent feeling, while she waited there in the shop, had been one of burning humiliation that she should be doomed, in her poor finery, to bring disgrace upon an honest place. "Imagine it!" she cried. "My silly silks—my silly shoes which dared not be wetted—my feathers and ribbons! And then he came riding up, full of real business, dressed for it——"

"Ah!" Mrs. Fox gasped.

"Dressed for it—his working clothes—no pretence upon him!" She turned her indignant face to her friend. "What right had I—what right has any person in the world, Mary, to act a doll at a child's tea-party? To play about, to trifle, and hinder the work of the world! Oh, I was utterly ashamed! I felt that I was despicable, worse than nothing before him."

"But he did not, I imagine."

"He was more than kind, he was noble; but he could not deny his own nature. He could not stoop to me, or make concessions. That is so wonderful in him, I think. I had seen it before when he stood up alone—inside the gates here—doing justice—inflexibly—with blood on his face. I felt the power of him break me down. I could have knelt to him."

"Dearest, I fear, I fear that you did."

"No, indeed. He would not have allowed it; and that made it all the worse, that I must pretend to confer and he to receive a favour. Favour from me to him! Oh, Mary, I went home burning—to my degradation, as I supposed. To be driven about in a carriage, splashing mud in the face of honesty with my hoofs and wheels; to be herded in a pack, among men who drank too much and women who wore too little; to gape at a conjurer, at pictures, at women jigging; to be fed by powdered giants, and be sung to by hired Italians! What a life to lead in a busy world! I was spared all that by grand-mamma, who locked me up—and gave me time to think of him. But in a day or two I had to go on with it all, as if nothing had happened. But, Mary, something *had* happened, something very wonderful. . . ." She frowned at Mary Fox, biting her red lip. "I don't see why one should do all this—I don't see how one dare do it, if one feels, if one knows that men and women are leading real lives outside; working, being happy in their work. They sing, Mary, as they go about their business. You hear them in the streets. Some of them used to whistle as they came to the house, and Jacobs always stopped them at the gates. No whistling at Caryll House—a sort of church! Oh, it's all wrong, it's all wrong! But now it's over, for me."

There spoke, perhaps, her father's child, and her mother's; offspring of that night's work in '88, when the silken lady of the Carylls rode pillion in the dark behind the man who had dared to break his sword. Had not this girl, too, caught at Reality by the knees?

The struggle went on with varying fortunes. Mary Fox was only half convinced, when the little sophist gained an unlooked-for arm for her warfare. She was able to confront the poor lady with a dilemma when the Earl of Morfa returned to town and brought his countess with him. The noble pair took a furnished house in Curzon Street—since nothing could, of course, be done to the dowager's detriment—and there they throve, in spite of all conclusions. The Family remained true to its patriarchal principle, that it is the male who ennobles. What then? A Countess Harriet is certainly a countess, while a Mrs. Hermia is a butcher's wife. Mary Fox, accepting that, gave her beloved a rhetorical advantage which she made the most of. Take hold of which prong you will, here are two, says Hermia. Either Harriet, who had been nobody, was made somebody by Uncle Roddy; or Uncle Roddy, who was supposed to be somebody, was made nobody by Harriet Moon. In the former case, why should she and Vernour between them not be somebody? In the latter, why should Uncle Badlesmere and Uncle John Botetort, and Aunt Carinthia, and Aunt Barwise, and Aunt Sarah Coigne, and even poor dear Uncle Bernard, all flock to Curzon Street and pay their respects to—nobody? Here were two horns for the impaling of Mary Fox, who, for her part (as the lawyers say), "confessed and avoided." She took Hermia, in-

deed, on the girl's initiative, to wait upon the new countess, an agitating encounter in more ways than one.
There was quite an assembly; the Earl not present.
Countess Harriet used her fine eyes with tact. She was
exceedingly kind to her former friend; but naturally
nothing was said about Hermia's affairs or her own.
There were no confidences, and never could be again—
because they had been all upon Harriet's side, and nearly
all untrue. It was Miss Chambre's first appearance in
the world since her disgrace, and she bore the trial with
a simplicity and complete absence of shamefacedness
which enchanted Mrs. Fox. But women are not self-
conscious. Look, for instance, at the Countess Harriet
chatting with Sir George Coigne, and contrast the two.

"Harriet told fibs," Hermia owned as they walked homewards, over the park to Brompton, "and very nearly
made me tell one. I suppose she had to defend herself
with what she had. And she always had fibs, I fancy.
She certainly led me to suppose that she would marry
George Coigne—and him, too, poor man."

So much, so far as I am concerned, of the Countess
Harriet, who had not, perhaps, done so badly for her
little hand. Sir George Coigne, the gossips say, was
there a great deal; but she never gave him the slightest
encouragement. I believe that she made Earl Roderick
an excellent wife. And now for serious news.

CHAPTER XXXII

IT was Ranald who told it to her—after she had been a week at Brompton—that Vernour and two others with him had been arrested, and lay in Newgate, for inciting to riot at the Westminster meeting. It touched his own honour, he said, nearly; he had done his best to get included in the charge. It had been his meeting, convened in his own constituency, on behalf of his colleague, for which he alone was responsible. He had offered to stand his trial, but no notice had been taken; and neither he nor Wardle would be touched. Of course, he would defend the men—she might rely upon him.

Her calmness was remarkable; for though she had not had a word from her lover since her avowal and disgrace, and for the two days before this news had not received her violets, she had been unalterably cheerful, extraordinarily happy—singing about the house, sewing, gossiping with Mary Fox, shopping—and had seen no omens even in the absence of her flowers. The intelligence ought to have knocked her over, she ought to have winced or paled; but it did neither. On the contrary, her colour had quickened, her eyes flashed. "Absurd!" she had said. "He will be acquitted." Then Ranald was

bound to tell her his fears. Sandgate and he would do
all that was possible, but she ought to prepare herself
for a bad verdict. There had undoubtedly been what
amounted to a riot; windows had been broken; an informer had been mauled, a constable hurt, not seriously,
but they would make the most of it. Vernour had been
the first to speak of spies; he had pointed his finger,
and mutterings had followed. Not much in that, but it
would count against him. The worst of all was that
Ministers intended to get a conviction. They had been
after one for years, ever since old Tooke's triumph; and
the haste with which they were pushing on now showed
what they thought of their chances. There would also
be other influences at work—she would understand that.

She did. "You mean my family's?"

He nodded. "Badlesmere is dead against you. And, of
course, her ladyship——" But she stopped him there.

"Grandmamma knows nothing of it. I am sure of
that."

"Well," he said, "I hope you are right. Then Roddy
will be generous, perhaps."

"Generous, Mr. Ranald!"

"Well, your Vernour pommelled him, you know, in his
own court—and Roddy's young, and as sensitive as most
youths."

She waived Roddy and his youth, having other things
to think of.

"Mr. Ranald," she asked, "ought I to go to him?"

"He won't hear of it. He didn't want me to tell you of this—in fact, he said, 'Here's the end of it,' directly he saw me. I talked him over into seeing that you must needs have the news sooner or later—and better from a friend than an enemy. But he has a horror of involving you in the business, as is only reasonable; and I think that you should humour him."

Her eyes were full. "Of course, I am involved—of course, it is my right to be involved. But I won't go until he sends for me. How long before they——?"

"Not long. They are in a hurry. He'll be taken before the magistrates in a month, and committed. They'll oppose bail, undoubtedly, but we'll try for it."

"And then——?"

"Trial next term, for certain. Ellenborough sits—that is settled."

She stared at the day, and at the days to come. "Lord Ellenborough! It means—no hope."

"Almost that—in these times. You will need all your courage—courage for two."

"I have the courage of two," she said. "I have his."

She wrote him a letter, which Ranald took. "One word from you, and I come. I am free here with Mary Fox, who would take me to and from your prison. I am in your hands, at your knees, and have no fear but to displease or trouble you. Oh, my love, I am proud that I can sit here and wait. HERMIA MARY—yours."

Ranald put it into his breast-pocket. "He shall have it, trust me. Let me say that I admire your spirit, and find it well mated. Good-bye for the moment." He kissed her hand.

It was that high spirit that won over Mary Fox, and vanquished all her doubts. No tears, no brooding, no quarter asked of heaven. "If they imprison him, he will bear it, and so must I. The time will pass—we are both quite young. And in any case we must have waited. I am grandmamma's property for five years—no, for four years more. That means that I should have been a sort of prisoner—not allowed to speak or write to him. Well, I should have borne that, and so would he." This girl was of heroic build—this girl of the thrust bosom and starry eyes. She won friends fast, as the story became known, though they were not of the kind who could have been acceptable at Caryll or Crowland House. Of her old allies, Lady Grizel was for her, Lord Sandgate, of course, and Ranald. Sir Francis wrote to her from the Tower, and the veteran Parson Tooke from his Wimbledon cavern. These things elated her—or she made the most of them. Nobody knew with what looming shapes she fought when she was alone; for there were no signs of the strife in the morning when she appeared at the breakfast table and kissed her Mary Fox. It was at that hour that she made what she could of her friends and alliances. She saw Ranald nearly every day; his devotion was exemplary.

Vernour and his companions were committed, having reserved their defence. No bail could be allowed. She had not been present, by his desire, or command, as she chose to call it—for just now when he was powerless and shadowed by infamy, her loyalty would have made him out a despot, if he had not taken that high road of his own accord. But he had written to her the night before he was to appear, a letter—not long—which shows clearly that arrogance had grown upon him with disgrace. Terseness was his vein, and a repression of feeling which might well have seemed cavalier to a less pliant mistress.

"My beloved," he wrote, "I must bid you farewell for a season which must be long, and shall be as much longer as you please. They will condemn me, I am sure; but that is little. There is another assize in which I am judge, jury, and prisoner, and in which I condemn myself. I shall ask no reprieve here. What I have of yours you will never take from me; but what you have left I will never take from you unless you bid me. Your lover."

She didn't see that it was an arrogant letter, that the signature in particular was extremely arrogant. It assumed entire dominion, not only of her heart and destiny, but of the hearts and needs of all men. "Your lover"! And she with a dozen lovers! It was on a par with the *Yo el Rey* of Spanish kings. Yet the poor girl kissed it often, and wore it faint in her bosom.

As for the preliminaries, Ranald gave her an account of them. Only one witness had been called—a Mr. Banks, a critic and historian. Mr. Banks? she had echoed, a Mr. Aloysius Banks? Yes, that was the party—cavernous kind of a man with a booming voice, who "deemed it to have been his painful duty to be present at an assembly of persons who"—that sort of a man.

She said that she knew him. He was the first Englishman she had spoken with upon landing, two years ago. "I have met him since, too. He used to come to the house. I asked granny to send him a card for a party. I believe he dined. I thought he liked me."

"He likes your family," said Ranald; but she did not catch the implication.

Banks, he thought, would be an awkward customer. There was this about his testimony which he did not tell her. He had seen Banks come into court between two noble lords. The Marquis of Badlesmere was one—Lady Morfa's brother—and Lord Barwise the other, Lady Morfa's son-in-law. Now, how could Banks be cross-examined with effect if you had to leave out Lords Badlesmere and Barwise, and their relations with the witness? Banks was an informer, of course—but who were his principals? Not the executive, Ranald thought; he was not of their camp. Then it must be Caryll House, acting through Lords Badlesmere and Barwise; and, in that case, the defence was tongue-tied.

The defence did what it could. Sir Samuel Romilly

had been retained, and Mr. Brougham. Then darkness settled down upon the Brompton lodgings, and Mary Fox lost flesh, anxious for her friend.

The case came on in June—middle of June—and made some stir, because, in spite of everything Ranald could do, the accessory facts became known. London rang with them: the newspapers, the ballad-sellers, the print-sellers, all the "damned tinker's pack of curs" were on to it, and noses down, tracked the scent. It made for the popularity of Vernour, as Ranald owned; it settled his private affairs; it made the prospects of Mr. Banks less rosy. Lord Sandgate took it upon himself to overlook the briefs: Mr. Banks's noble friends were not forgotten. He did more. He instructed Cobbett, he instructed the *Examiner*, and in a speech which he made in the City on the eve of the trial he did not scruple to allude to the romantic circumstances under which this accomplished young man and hopeful citizen became involved in a snare of public malice and private rancour to parallel which he must needs have searched the Register of *Lettres de cachet*, happily burned with their partner in infamy, the Bastille. The town caught at the allusion and wormed out the romantic circumstances. Back came the butcher's horse, the visit to Brook Street; back the "Lad in blue," and the "Lady in white"; back the famous print, "Cob-it, my hearty!" And this was the eve of the trial.

She watched out the day with Mary Fox. She did not

cry, but she could not pretend to courage. She had far rather have been present: the thing was how to get through the hours. At twelve o'clock she got up and went for a walk; but she had the fancy that everybody was looking at her and had to come back. It is the fact that she had seen the unhallowed print in a bookseller's window, and was unnerved by it. She told Mary that if somebody had slapped her on the cheek, she would have got her courage back. And so it happened: somebody did.

At five, or half after, from her window she saw Mr. Ranald ride up to the door, and turned to wait for him, holding her heart.

He was shown in, and she received him standing. No greetings passed.

"You will need your courage," he said.

She had nothing to say.

"They've found him guilty, the hounds—but we've got old Banks into the mire." Her eyes asked, not her lips.

"The thing is atrocious. Ellenborough! Licking his lips before he began—like a wolfish usher with his cane. Miss Chambre, he has six months and a fine of £250."

She laughed aloud. "That! To us!"

He added, "There's more. He's to stand three hours in the pillory, and put all England to shame. By God, I wish I were in his shoes! We'd bring down Northumberland House about their ears."

This was her slap on the face. The hot blood spread. "When is this to be?"

"To-morrow week, at Charing Cross. Oh, the ingenuity of these rascals! The House rises that day—do you see? If there's a row, they can do their work quietly— no questions asked—and Burdett comes out, too. Oh, they've worked it well. A row there'll be. But you must be out of this."

"I shall go, of course," she said; and he could have kissed her.

CHAPTER XXXIII

LORD RODONO was the first to hear of it. He was in the lobby of the House, which was about to be prorogued by a king's speech, and had just divided. In these days he had lived very much to himself, unknown to his usual haunts, missed alike at Brooks's, Newmarket, Crowland House. He held by the House of Commons, because a man must do something, and because he felt that he must stay on, somehow, and "see the end." He knew all about the trial, naturally, and the end of it; he raged over the scandal, and loathed all the actors in it. Hermia herself was cheapened and soiled—and yet "the pity! the pity!" He had not been face to face with her since that evening in the spring when she was brought to Clarges Street by—— Oh, damn it, the thing was hideous!

But he had followed everything since his battle with Vernour, when he had acknowledged the man's integrity; he had known where Hermia was living, had allowed Ranald to talk of her and her prospects, had seen Ranald getting deeper and deeper into her graces, and deeper and deeper into need of them. Bob Ranald was "one of us" by now. Not in the running—nobody had a ghost of a chance beside that accursed butcher—but running, apparently, for glory and honour—for the sake of her whom he called the "starriest girl in all England." Rodono felt that he could have been Ranald's best man with pride and thanksgiving; but the butcher—oh, God! No, a woman, to be perfect in his eyes, must be unspotted from the world, cloistered and approached only on the knees—by all men but one.

Some such thoughts as these—constant with him at the time—filled him now as he ground his heel into the pavement and sunk his hands deeper into his breeches pockets.

"She's mired herself—she's draggled—faugh! what a maid fell there! Bewitched, besotted, beguiled, betrayed! What a high head—and down it droops! What a bold flight—toppled, shot in the breast!"

A man came through the lobbies, rather breathless, news in his face. He was triumphant over his little grain of knowledge.

Rodono stood alone, his hat over his eyes, and the newcomer caught sight of him. Something was wrong with Tom, who cut his old friends—now, if one could wake him up! One might try. The man of news stopped.

"I say, Tom, my boy, there's a rare row—Cobbett's at it—and the Orator, foaming at the mouth."

"Ah!" said Rodono, "I dare say. What else? Anything new? Where's your row, Cassonby?"

"Charing Cross—over the butcher's carcase." That pricked him.

"What do you mean—carcase? They've not——?"

Mr. Cassonby tossed his whiskered face. "Good Lord, no. ' Otherwise. They're ready to break up the pillory. She's there, you know."

"She?" What eyes Rodono had! Cold steel! Mr. Cassonby knew better than to quote the ballads, of which he had a stock.

"Miss Chambre's there," he said. "Facing 'em all. They treat her like a queen."

Tom Rodono was certainly in Queer Street, as Mr. Cassonby informed the next man he met. "I was telling him a devilish good story—putting it devilish well, too— for I was moved, sir, dammy, I was moved—and off he goes as if shot from a gun. I saw the lady come—she's been there three-quarters of an hour. Came with Bob Ranald—on the arm of Bob—and a veiled friend. Bob clears the road as he'd clear decks. 'Way there, my lads, way there,' says Bob, humouring the fellows—you know Bob! So she comes up through a lane of them as if she was at a drawing-room—and stands underneath the stage, and faces 'em all. And Bob—little Bob—he keeps a clear space for her—marches up and down, true quarter-deck fashion. Oh, it was rare! They cry three cheers for 'Lady Vernour,' if you please. Lady Vernour! They marry her and raise her to the peerage all in a breath—that's what we're coming to with our blessed Reform. The mob'll make peers when they've unmade a few. You'll see. . . . Lady Vernour! . . .

Up comes old Cobbett on horseback—they give him room enough—and rope enough, hey? He was haranguing when I left. But she was rare—never flinched, never blinked—just did what she had to do—and stuck to it, sir—kept on with it."

All this Tom Rodono had missed; but going down Westminster Hall he could not miss Lord Sandgate, who met him full.

They had not had much to say to each other of late, and what there had been to say bore no reference to Miss Chambre's affair. Lord Sandgate was by nature reserved, and in consequence suspicious of reserve in other men's dealings with him. He had striven hard in Vernour's defence, the reader knows, and had made so bold as to drag in the Caryll House faction for the scarifying of Mr. Banks. He suspected, not without reason, that Rodono did not praise him for this, and kept out of his colleague's neighbourhood. He would have passed him now with a nod had not something in the fierce striding of the man caught his attention—something fell in his purpose. As it was, he stopped him.

"Where are you going, Tom?"

Rodono met his eye without, at first, seeming to recognise him; but he, too, stopped, and a dullish hue of grey spread over his face. Rodono, his temper lost, had a devil.

"You've a right to know, I suppose. I'm going to her."

"Ha! Where is she?"

"At your pillory, my lord. Where you drove her to be."

"You have no right to say that—but I can't quarrel with you now. I come with you."

"You can do as you please," said Rodono. Before they had reached the Horse Guards, they could hear the roaring of the mob at Charing Cross.

Squalid splendour, or homely strength, whichever you please, have always marked our country, which can choose to rule a share of two worlds from a little brown house in Downing Street. Squalor beyond description vile was spread broad over the field at Charing Cross where, on that midsummer day, the pageant of an offended realm was displayed. And yet the scene as viewed from afar did not lack in force of character. From the entry of Whitehall you might have seen it enacted in dumb show, by creatures less than men; for the ground ran up from Westminster, and no staging, no crucificial gallows could make headway against the great mass of Northumberland House. So our two gentlemen saw it, as a scene, above the swarming masses of men, between tossing flags, caps in the air, flung-up hands— dumbly done amidst a hubbub of hoarse voices—waxing and waning like a heavy sea—now angry, gathering, and low—hooting Castlereagh or Canning—and anon swelling into a roar of cheers as some popular name was

thrown upon the waves. Above and beyond all this, upon
a wooden platform stood the crosses, as they seemed; the
tau-shaped gallows-trees wherefrom three fixed faces
stared, and six hands drooped helpless and unhappily
white. About stood the sheriffs' officers and the constables—a short person in a gown and cocked hat seemed
to be reading a proclamation; and at the further fringe
of the crowd a broad-shouldered rider, his hat waving in
his hand, was roaring himself hoarse in rivalry. The
windows of the ducal house were full—ladies were there,
and gentlemen—some in uniform. The rest was sun-
glare, dust, and flung-up arms; and over all the rising
surge of noise, now angry, now wild in triumph.

"Come," said Lord Sandgate, "or we shall be too late."
Rodono needed no prompting; he was in front, battling
a way through. The outskirts here were easy—dandies
on horseback making bets—traders with limp ballads,
wet from the press, chariots, with ladies standing on the
box-seat, a juggler with a white rabbit, pick-pockets,
beggars, and harsh-faced women, draggle-tailed and
tousle-haired. Beyond this fringe Rodono had to use
his shoulders, then his voice. He descended to working
with his own name, and was rewarded with a "God bless
you, my lord," and room made. He was not known—but
Lord Sandgate fared better. "Let my lord go through
—the people's friend"—and a cheer for Reform.

It was Sandgate at last who led the way; his name
carried further than his title—but it could not work

miracles. To cleave that jammed mass of sweating, roaring humanity he must use a sharper weapon, and not scruple. "Let us pass, if you please—we are going to the lady. We are friends—let us pass." "Lady Vernour! God bless her ladyship! Make room—make room!" Thus they made their way, and saw the stout Captain Ranald striding up and down the cockpit he had cleared—saw his alert, authoritative eyes, his squared jaw, his weathered cheeks — heard his comfortable "Steady there, my lads, and keep the peace"—and saw then the pale girl, in her white dress, a veil about her brows, standing calm, unfaltering, and steady-eyed—like Mary at the foot of the cross.

The bitterness, the shamefulness, the gall! Rodono went white to the lips. He turned on Sandgate and smote him with his anger. "You've done this, you damned procurer; you're answerable for this!" His voice was a sword.

But Lord Sandgate did not flinch. "I'll answer you anywhere but here. At present we've a duty—to her. If I did, I'm proud of it." He hoped that he was.

She made no sign when they came and stood one on each side of her and her veiled friend, Mary Fox; it seemed that she had got beyond the stage of consciousness; as though all her nerves and faculties, bent before to the one task of endurance, were now set hard; as though she stood because she was stiffened. No one spoke. Gradually Rodono also stiffened, and lost his burning sense of wrong done. The million-eyed, surging, hoarsely murmuring sea tossed before him unheeded; he, too, was learning how best to endure. Of them all, the one person who kept his wits about him was the fever-taut Ranald.

There was plainly no danger to be feared from those in front. The beauty, the stillness, and the dignity of the young girl held the mob's eyes and subdued its tongue. It would as soon have intruded upon one dead. But the pressure from behind was very serious, and from the sides came now and again an ugly sound. On the steps of the Golden Cross over the Strand, speaker after speaker stood up—shouted, gesticulated, pointed this way and that, all in dumb show, and was answered by a roar. No stones were thrown, and there was, on the whole, more good-humoured admiration for the victims than rage against the officers. This was the state of affairs at half-past four, when Rodono had been with her half an hour. There was another hour to go yet; and a diversion was approaching from Cockspur Street— a four-horse open chariot was making its way through the crowd at the back. You could see now and again the fretful crests of the horses, the bobbing white hats of postilions, the heads of the two footmen, with staves, swaying behind; and above all this the coachman in three-cornered hat and wig. You could tell by the bending of his shoulders that he was humouring his cattle, and in a mortal terror.

The crowd divided—some hats went off, there was some cheering, but not much. Anyhow, there was no hooting, and the liveries were not scarlet. Rodono, who had thought one of the Princesses might have blundered into the thing, or that one, in particular, might have chosen to brazen her case before such a mob, was puzzled and intrigued. Was it a rescue? Was it—could it be—? By the Lord Harry, but it was! The carriage came on by inches at a time—and now he could see the single, nodding occupant. Her dowager ladyship of Morfa was come to take her share, and his heart went out to the old, white eagle-face. "By God, the old wolf will fight for her cubs!"

The Morfa chariot it was which made its way to the foot of the scaffold. Even so Hermia had to be told. Ranald told her, after he had exchanged a word or two with her ladyship.

The old Countess, after nodding and blinking at her girl—and in vain—had beckoned him up. "Get her in, Mr. Ranald. She can't stop here."

"I fear, my lady, that she means it. I can't force her."

"Ask her to speak to me. Let this be stopped."

"I'll ask her."

He spoke to her, he touched her on the arm. "Your grandmother wishes to speak to you. She has come here." Hermia seemed to awake out of her dream at that.

"Where is grandmamma?"

"Here—in the carriage."

"Give me your arm, please." He took her up. The mob craned and surged, then swept back to give her place.

"Hermia, child," said her ladyship, "I implore you to come with me."

She shook her head. "Not now, granny—not yet." The old lady moistened her dry lips.

"I'm an old woman, my dear—and I ask it of you." Hermia had tears in her eyes, for the first time that day.

"You know that I would come—if I could. Oh, granny, my place is there!"

"We cannot argue—we cannot talk of these things, my child."

"No, no."

"I have come for you—I have brought myself so far— and I am an old woman."

"Dearest granny—if I could! But—ah, you must not ask me to leave—David." Shaking head and blinking eyes—the old eagle of a woman. Old as she was, she whipped herself forward.

"I wish to say—I have come to say—that I knew nothing of this. I have been ill. They told me nothing."

She had never supposed it—had not been told of Banks's alliances. Truth and candour beamed in her eyes, as she answered, "No, no, granny. I am sure—I am quite sure." But she would not come—she could not.

Therefore, Lady Morfa sat it out, and Hermia went back to her post.

The dragoons, who had been sent for at half-past three, came down Cockspur Street, and were first seen by Vernour—the midmost of the cruciform wretches, staring there dry-tongued and dizzy. He made inarticulate noises in his throat, which were heard by a constable, and, oddly enough, attended to. The man was a good fellow.

"Are you ill, Mr. Vernour? Are you ill, sir?"

"No, no," said Vernour. "The soldiers. Take her away. Get her away."

Ranald saw him contorting up there, and went to him. No one stopped him. He mounted the platform. Vernour repeated his order. "Tell her to go—it is my desire. There is terrible work coming." Ranald looked, and saw it coming. Plain enough to his practised eye. The people had faced the soldiery, but did not budge. Oaths and fierce cries from the midst were heard. The officer in command had a restive horse; here were the elements of something grim.

"Yes, yes, Vernour; she ought to go—and the carriage, too. Good God, that old dragon of a lady! You desire her—to go?" He motioned with his eyes—he was nearly done. Ranald went down and spoke to Hermia, who looked up in alarm, and wavered, swayed about.

She recovered in a moment, and wavered no more. She went up the ladder, in a tense silence from all who could see her; Ranald followed. She had a little phial of brandy in her hand, and went to him with it. She fed him, drop by drop, and whispered to him—none heard what she said. She succoured the other two, one of whom, a mere boy, was bending at the knees.

Ranald spoke to the sheriff. "Take these men down, sir. There'll be murder here." The sheriff was very much perplexed.

"I can't take orders from you, Mr. Ranald."

"You get them straight from hell, I think. How much more of this is there to be?"

He got no answer, and expected none. He saw that the stones were flying—and remarked also that the murmur was lulled so that you could hear the sharp order of the officer, and the rattle of arms, as the men obeyed. "By God, they're going to fire!"

A man galloped up to the officer and spoke to him. Immediately afterwards, a stone hit him on the head— Ranald saw him cower sideways and clap up his hand to his face.

All heads were turned towards the coming battle; the crowd, led as it always is by its front, was pushing towards the dragoons. Vernour gasped out his command—"Go, Hermia, go!"—two of the constables spoke to her. Orders were peremptory—she must leave the platform. She turned—she dared not look at her lover, for fear of his terrible, tortured face and glazing eyes— but she was wild, and knew not what she was doing. She raised her face—a pale, tragic face it was—and kissed the helpless hand near her; and then suffered herself to be led away.

She was not a moment too soon. By the time she had been put into the carriage with Mary Fox, and the horses turned to Whitehall, the mob was surging up to meet the dragoons—the scaffold and its burden were almost deserted. She saw—it was the last thing she saw—the three crosses stand up against Northumberland House, as it were in a desert place; and then she fainted. She did not hear the volley which ended the day's work. Ranald had to tell her of that, and said that he had never guessed before what a coward he was.

CHAPTER XXXIV

I CLOSE with what scattered notes I have left, to account as best I can for the remaining maiden years of Miss Chambre's life. Her story, however, so far as my present purposes are concerned, was virtually told with the shot which ended Vernour's earthly course. She lived them, I understand, mainly, if not altogether, in the country: at Wrensham, whither the Dowager Lady Morfa retreated before the advance of the new Countess; in Ireland, with the George Foxes; rarely at Petersham; and, for one visit certainly, in the west of Scotland, where Lord and Lady Clanranald occupied a scarred fortalice —"as poor as rats and as keen as rats-bane," was the description of his parents given her by Captain Ranald, heir of the ragged demesne. "A pair of old ravens," some other wag termed them, "sitting on a scaur, looking sideways for death." They were very kind to the girl, and liked her. They reported her docile and affectionate. Docile and affectionate!—Hermia Mary! This must have been, the reader sees, a long time after her fiery ordeal. It was, in fact, nearly three years afterwards, when Bob Ranald's hopes were high, and the wounded amazon more resigned to her lot.

Poor young Vernour, shot by a chance ball of that volley which she had not heard, was forgotten by the world
which had been ready to make much of him, given a
favouring star. There had been an inquest, at which
Ranald made a scene, and did his best to get committed;
there had been regrets from the Home Office, and a talk
of prosecution—but none followed. The law officers
were clear on the points; it could not be denied that the
Riot Act had been read, stones thrown, the cheek of a
sheriff of Middlesex cut open. Besides, who did the
deed? How can you indict a squadron? Was it to be
supposed that any hand had been murderously, deliberately levelled at a man tied in the pillory? Nothing was
done; as Ranald had said, the day had been well chosen.
Parliament was up that day; Sir Francis was enlarged;
within a week Mr. Cobbett was standing to answer a
charge of libel, and within three weeks he was in gaol.
These were timely diversions, and confounded the popular party. Vernour was no longer a handle for Lord
Sandgate's battle-axe. Lord Sandgate, indeed, dropped
him. Better for his uses an imprisoned Cobbett than a
dead Vernour.

But my Lord Sandgate could not so easily drop Tom
Rodono, whose affair with him marks the end of a painful scandal. It had a paragraph in *The Morning Post*,
and half a column in the *Examiner*. *The Morning
Chronicle*, which was the Whig organ, did not notice it
at all. The gentlemen met on Wimbledon Common, on

the morning of that day on which they buried Vernour;
Lord Morfa was Rodono's second. They exchanged a
shot apiece, and Sandgate fired first—but wide. Rodono
hit him in the shoulder, and, it is thought, nicked the
bone. However, both combatants rode off the ground,
after expressing themselves in becoming terms.

After the dismal rites were done, she fell into a state of
listlessness and apathy. She did not cry (not being of
the sort that gets relief that blessed way), and was perfectly amiable, but she was without a will of her own—
except on one point, and that an odd one. Nothing could
tempt her to leave her grandmother for long, not even
the wooing of Mary Fox, of green Kilbride, and the
sweet, wet gales of Roscommon; she who had so stoutly
played the rebel was now an ardent Loyalist. True, the
fierce old woman was somewhat broken; true that she
quailed before the brown-eyed little Countess Harriet and
her array. "Moon-struck," they said, the stern old
warrior; and it's certain that she never met her daughter-
in-law in this world. So that it may have been pity which
touched the rebel heart—and, if so, that's to its credit;
but I believe that it was admiration. Steel fires steel. I
believe that it was the spectacle of the nodding old eagle
enduring the shame of London—the gaping, the nudg-
ing, the tongues in the cheeks—which spoke to her, as
it were, with a voice: Here is a franchise worthy of your
esteem, and here a pride above your own. Bend your
knee, Norman.

The Hon. Captain Ranald, while pursuing his political adventures, kept an eye open to what chances he might have of possessing his bruised goddess. He knew that they could only improve with time; but he intended to have her, if waiting patiently could help him. It was her spirit he loved, he told himself—the spirit she had once had—though her beauty, to his mind, was enhanced by the pale and pensive cast it wore. With these things won, he vowed that he should be content. "She'll never love me, I know," he told his friend Cliffe Jenyns, the traveller and poet. "She's the kind that gives once, and gives all. If I get her, it will be like marrying a nun."

"Not it, my boy," said the genial Cliffe, "if you are the man I believe you." But Ranald shook his head. "I'm not romantic, but I can see the vestal in her. God bless you, why do you suppose she tumbled into that young man's arms?"

"Fine fellow, you tell me, fine figure of a young man. Had parts—spoke well, could think—is that what you mean?"

Ranald snapped his fingers. "Pooh, sir, nothing of the sort! His greatest chance with her was that she knew nothing about him. It was all gossamer-web of her own spinning. The business was done on that visit of hers to Brook Street—you remember, I told you about that at the time—to apologise. Well, she was in a great fright, and no wonder. He got the benefit of that—don't you see? She was there to sing small, and she be-

came small; the smaller she, the greater he. As she
stooped, he towered up, higher and higher. She pro-
jected him as a god, and god he remained to the end of
the chapter. All a generous figment of her brain—I'm
sure of it. . . .

"Mind you, I knew Vernour well, and admired him.
He had character—a quiet force; and it did so happen
that he could make use of it. Politics! they had nothing
to do with the matter. She knew no politics except by
hearsay; if she had any leanings herself, it was towards
aristocracy. She was one to the tips of her finger-nails.
No; he struck her imagination, and she chose—as
queens used to choose. As for him—damn it, he was a
male."

Cliffe Jenyns laughed. "What are you, Bob, for instance—politician or male?"

"I don't say. It's not come to that—and I suppose
I'm a gentleman. What I mean is this—that there's a
field which politics can't touch, a fund in this old world
which will outlive science and all our blessed systems. I
agree with Tom Paine, of course—as far as he goes. If
a man is not finer than a king, God help the monarchy;
and if he is, why, God will stand aside. So down goes
the monarchy at the proper time. But there's a Right of
Man unconsidered by Tom; and I say that she lent herself to the proving of it. She submitted, she stooped to
be the test case. And, by God, she proved it."

"Do you mean that the eternal male——?"

"I do. He was no more than that essentially—splendid brawn. But she was the Divinity who submitted to a man—for us men. Democracy in practice! She took us a step beyond the Rights of Man, which we're all prating about, to the Rights of Nature, which will outlast all politics and politicians—when she, the noble, free-moving creature, in her own way, worked out the Right of Man— of any man who is one—to choose his mate. Other things being equal—as they were here—no caste can stand out against that. Had she been an archduchess, it would have made no difference."

"Your course is clear," said Jenyns. "Advance, man, and choose."

"Not now. She gave him all—as they do, my friend, as they do—and once for all. I shall get a shell, but I shall take it."

He stared at the fire, then broke out again. "She's the sort that must give, that thrives only so. She has breasts; she must feed the hungry. She stoops from her high seat and sheds heaven upon us; and it's not one in ten thousand that sees the condescension, the magnanimity, the extraordinary bounty. The Stooping Lady! The Stooping Lady! That's what I call her. . . . I'll tell you what it is, Cliffe; she'd have me to-morrow if she thought I was broken."

He was right there.

THE END.

SAMUEL ADAMS

SAMUEL ADAMS

PROMOTER OF THE AMERICAN REVOLUTION

A STUDY IN PSYCHOLOGY AND POLITICS

BY

RALPH VOLNEY HARLOW

OCTAGON BOOKS

A DIVISION OF FARRAR, STRAUS AND GIROUX

New York   1975

Reprinted 1975

by arrangement with Holt, Rinehart and Winston, Inc.

OCTAGON BOOKS

A DIVISION OF FARRAR, STRAUS & GIROUX, INC.

19 Union Square West

New York, N. Y. 10003

Library of Congress Cataloging in Publication Data

Harlow, Ralph Volney, 1884-1956.
    Samuel Adams, promoter of the American Revolution.

    Reprint of the ed. published by H. Holt, New York.
    1. Adams, Samuel, 1722-1803.   2. United States—Politics and
    government—Revolution, 1775-1783.

E302.6.A2H2   1975   973.3'092'4 [B]   75-1390
ISBN 0-374-93664-1

A po. 24, 1975

Printed in USA by
Thomson-Shore, Inc.
Dexter, Michigan

To

J. M. H.

In Settlement of a Wager long outstanding.

CONTENTS

PREFACE

In attempting a new biography of Samuel Adams, the writer's aim has been primarily to show the man at work, and to make clear, as far as possible, why he followed his particular course. The study deals, then, with the processes of the Revolution, with informal committees and extra-legal assemblages, with the manufacture of public opinion; in short, with the complicated, underground machinery necessary to all revolutions. Likewise it is concerned with the psychological side of revolution, with the "secret places of the heart" of the revolutionary personality. Perhaps the resort to analytical psychology will seem unwarranted on the part of a historian. If so, the writer would plead in extenuation that objective causes fail to give any adequate explanation of Adams's behavior; it becomes necessary therefore either to ignore the whole question of interpretation, or to adopt the only method that seems reasonable.

The writer is glad to acknowledge at this time his indebtedness to those who have made this biography possible. He first became interested in the subject several years ago, in the graduate seminar of Professor W. C. Abbot, who was then at Yale. At the same time he approached the same problem from a somewhat different point of view in the classes of Professor C. M. Andrews. To these names, the writer wishes to add that of Professor Ernest R. Groves, of the department of Sociology at Boston University, whose suggestions regarding the application of psychology to history have been most interesting and helpful.

It is likewise a pleasure to thank the librarians and attendants at the various libraries where material has been gathered, especially those at the American Antiquarian Society of Worcester, Massachusetts, at the Massachusetts Historical Society, and at the libraries of Harvard and Yale Universities.

Finally thanks are due to my wife, for never-failing interest and help in the none too easy task of writing. Her watchfulness has led to the elimination of many errors; her suggestions have made the book more readable; and her assistance in preparing the manuscript for the press has been invaluable. Had it not been for her help the book would have remained unfinished for no one knows how long.

R. V. H.

Needham, Massachusetts.
October, 1922.